QiGong

...a 'Qi Gong state' is a relaxed and attentive state. The mind has calmed down and is in a relaxed but concentrated focus on the exercise

QiGong

the Chinese art of working with energy

Barbara Brown and Günter Knöferl

Thorsons

Thorsons

Thorsons
An Imprint of HarperCollinsPublishers
77–85 Fulham Palace Road,
Hammersmith, London W6 8JB

The Thorsons website address is: www.thorsons.com

Published by Thorsons 2001

10 9 8 7 6 5 4 3 2 1

Editorial Director: Belinda Budge
Editor: Nicky Vimpany
Design: XAB
Production: Mell Vandevelde
Index: Susan Bosanko
Photographs by Guy Hearn

A catalogue record for this book is available from the British Library

ISBN 0 7225 3972 X

Printed in Hong Kong

ACKNOWLEDGMENTS

For Nick, Jason and Eva

We'd like to begin with a special and poignant recognition of Jean Cooper (J.C. Cooper), who died recently. Jean, in her nineties, living alone in the Lake District, was beloved to all of us who knew her for many years as the embodiment of Taoist humour, lightness and wisdom. We were due to visit her just two weeks before she died. Jean, thank you for the brilliant legacy you pass on to all your friends and readers.

Our respect and thanks to our teachers, Master Li Zhi Chang and Master Zhixing Wang, for the interviews they gave us, and for their inspired teaching. In their different ways they take us deep into Qi Gong, and we are delighted with their contribution to the book.

Words of appreciation for Kenneth S. Cohen whose writing radiates the spirit of Taoism. We found his book a most valuable resource, and we thank Ken for his prompt personal response to various questions.

We would like to thank all students who help us to become clear enough in what we are doing and communicating.

Thanks to colleagues and friends supporting us in the writing process, particularly John Solagbade and Margaret Gücklhorn.

Thank you to Nick Brown for bringing the manuscript into its final form.

Thank you to our editor, Belinda Budge for her commitment, encouragement and honesty.

CONTENTS

Introduction
Tao: No-thingness, and yet the Potential of All   viii

1 Qi Gong – Energy Work   1

2 Qi – Life Force   7
Approaching Qi
Pre- and Post-natal Qi
The Three Treasures
Jing, Qi, Shen

3 Qi Gong History   21
The Shamanistic Heritage
Early Chinese Medicine
The Monastic Tradition
Modern Times

4 Ingredients for Practice   35
Time and Place
Warm-up
The Qi Gong State
Posture
Breathing
Yi – The Guiding Mind
Ending
Disturbances
The Tao of Practice

5 Moving with Qi - Active Qi Gong   83
Circling the Ball
Punching
Carrying the Moon
Reaching and Grounding
Flying Wild Goose
A Brief Word about the Classics

6 Being moved by Qi - Quiet Qi Gong   97
Microcosmic Orbit
Inner Smile
Buddha Breathing
The Three Belly Circles
Meridian Circle

**7 Letting Qi do its Work – Spontaneous
Qi Gong**   115

8 Healing with Qi   123

9 Integrating Qi Gong into Daily Life   135
Practice without Practice
Doing Qi Gong in Nature
The Bedroom Arts
Finding a Teacher

**10 BodyTao – Body Psychotherapy meets
Qi Gong**   149
Body Psychotherapy and Qi Gong Working Together
Walking the Figure Eight
Cultivating Emotions

**11 Interviews with Master Zhixing Wang and
Master Li Zhi Chang**   165

12 Information   173
Glossary
List of Exercises
Bibliography
Contacts
Index

TAO: NO-THINGNESS, AND YET THE POTENTIAL OF ALL

In the text, we often refer to Taoism, the Tao, Taoist sages. For this word – pronounced 'Dao' – there is no explanation, no translation. The Taoists say you cannot describe the indescribable – it Just Is. Having thus alluded to the indescribable and declared that you can't describe it, Taoism artfully continues to point at it, to hint at it, to express the knowingness and unknowingness of it.

Living in the Tao – or living in things exactly as they are, living in yourself exactly as you are – can be experienced by standing on Earth and feeling its supportive, material, nourishing function, and feeling the breath of Heaven within us and around us.

The Great Mystery of the Tao, the Source of Manifestation, is Unknowable. The reality of the Unknowable is left to Itself. We humans, part of the whole cycle of life, can only read the Mystery through its manifestation. As we

ourselves are manifestations of the Tao, the laws of the Tao move through every level of our being. To live in the Tao is a way inwards, a way of self-experience or self-enquiry: not an intellectual task, but an experience of greater intelligence, intelligence of body-mind-spirit. We are motivated and guided by longing, a longing for balance, for harmony, for knowledge of our essential selves. This longing pours out and has been expressed through poetry, music, prayer, meditation, dance and ritual, throughout the continuing saga of human history.

Taoism supports us with guidelines and maps – from the superb Tao te Ching to breathing exercises. The Taoist spirit – simplicity, silence, emptiness and naturalness – prevails through all instruction and expression. If you open up and surrender to the Tao – from this place of emptiness Tao can work through you. Wu-wei: not forcing but accepting things as they are, and acting accordingly.

Living in the Tao – or living in things exactly as they are, living in yourself exactly as you are – can be experienced by standing on Earth and feeling its supportive, material, nourishing function, and feeling the breath of Heaven within us and around us. As humans we are the living mediator between the forces of Earth and Heaven – Yin and Yang. And then, microcosm from macrocosm, we are the macrocosm in miniature, a universe unto ourselves with ecology, weather systems, interconnecting organs within a sea of fluid; energetic and nervous highways carrying information and communication. Our inner eco-system is many-layered and

includes matter, energy and spirit. It can become dry, too hot, too damp, too cold, out of balance – as a cosmos in miniature, we are subjected to the same forces we experience 'outside' of us.

Our world, our lives, are governed by relativity and change. The visible world, the invisible world, body and spirit are all part of an unfolding One, which continues to birth itself and die, to go through its cycles of death and regeneration, to follow its day with night, its spring with summer. The Tao is expressed in the endless stream of interactive polarities that pours from the One. Yin and Yang are the opposites of manifestation, primal polarities that constantly relate, creating and re-creating each other. To live in the Tao is to live within polarities, and, more deeply, to live with the Undivided Oneness at the root of all polarity.

Qi Gong is designed as a way to experience Tao in action, through cultivating life-energy. Through direct experience, Qi Gong points to the joy of being able to know the energies, cycles, little lives and deaths of the organism. The gentle, rhythmic movements reflect Yin and Yang in an ongoing, harmonious flow, quietly undoing the stagnation, interruption or violence of polarities sick at heart with each other. Qi Gong teaches that polarities are not only opposite to each other, but present and embedded within each other. The black fish has a white eye; the white fish has a black eye.

X

The practice cultivates an acceptance of things as they are. Instead of trying to bolster ourselves up and make ourselves different and better, we allow our whole being to settle into its Taoist nature, its wish for harmony and balance. As weather blows through us, we bend and submit, knowing that the weather changes. We accept ourselves as we are, and then we accept that we also have the capacity to be cultivators of our own energy. We can enhance the energy that has been given to us not only through exercise and awareness, but also through feeding directly from the clear air on mountain tops or the rhythm of waves at the ocean's edge, from the inner sweetness of spirit as it move us through our consciousness and expressions of the heart.

Life-energy is called qi. All-pervasive, qi is a movement mysterium throughout nature. Without qi we lose life. When qi is no longer there, we cannot bring it back. The rising and falling of breath, the penetration and reception of masculine and feminine forces, the movements of energy, are the pulses that constitute the basic alphabet of life. The Taoist is a participatory investigator of everyday miraculous phenomena, penetrating to the very bone marrow of the process and finding ways of co-existing inside these phenomena as they unfold. The Taoist is aware of the presence of the indefinable 'That' as it unfolds implicitly in all – and as it disappears mysteriously, unknowably, into the Beyond.

氣

1

Qi Gong - Energy Work

At dawn, by the riverside, in the park. Figures in groups, or alone, young and old, men and women. Dressed in loose, comfortable clothes. Though their eyes are open, there is an inward focus, an internal listening. The knees are flexible, slightly bent; the head rests quietly and straight upon the neck; the arms move slowly up and down, left and right in calm, quiet sweeping movements. The body bends gradually from the waist, circling lightly around the stability of the legs and feet. There is an atmosphere of relaxation, leisure and release; of concentration and focus. Archetypally, these images emerge from China. Nowadays the practice of Qi Gong has become internationally popular.

The observer, not yet initiated into the working principles of Qi Gong, can nonetheless identify elements of the tradition: slow, regular, graceful, repetitive movements, sometimes minimal or ceasing altogether; the gentle rising and falling of the body indicating easy and relaxed breathing. Not so much the outward performance of an exercise, but rather an activity carrying with it an aura of privacy.

Being relaxed and focused at the same time lies at the heart of Qi Gong. This might seem paradoxical to a Western observer but it is also the paradox of the Tao: activity generated from stillness; let go in order to do; soft equals strong; effortless effort.

The term Qi Gong was created in the 1950s to cover theories and practices of energy cultivation.

The roots of these many practices reach back to prehistoric times. Throughout its long history, Qi Gong has developed an immense diversity of styles and forms. Qi Gong can be simple. It can be exquisitely varied and complex. From simplicity to complexity, and through this diversity, it is possible to identify common features.

✦ postures and movement

Qi Gong can be done lying down, sitting, standing or moving. Sometimes there is no perceptible outer movement, as the focus is fully on inner movement. Sometimes there is outer movement, simple or elaborate, usually slow and gentle. These movements suggest that the surrounding air is of a liquid quality. The practitioner seems to move in water, to move like water; the air around the body is almost palpable, carrying an element of weight and resistance. Water is the essential Taoist metaphor in Qi Gong, appreciated for its yielding, and yet strong character.

✦ state of mind

A 'Qi Gong state' is a relaxed and attentive state. The mind has calmed down and is in a relaxed but concentrated focus on the exercise, not identifying with distracting inner dialogue. When the mind is calm, the inward experience is centred, peaceful and spacious. Focused awareness and visualization are used to guide qi – life energy.

✦ breath

There are different breathing techniques in Qi Gong, but the underlying emphasis is on naturalness. Generally, breathing is not forced, but its passage and movements are brought to awareness through attention, and softened through relaxation.

The most simple translation of Qi Gong is 'energy work'. While 'energy work' is also used in the West for techniques in the therapeutic and esoteric field, Qi Gong is embedded in a distinctly Chinese way of life. A key word is balance: as an ideal, the human being is in balance within, in balance with others and in balance with the outer world, Heaven and Earth. This ideal is a picture, a notion. It is not life as we live it. Balance is a dynamic principle. Life as process and change manifests the ever-flowing polarities of Yin and Yang. Qi is the main force in a process of constantly organizing and re-organizing our inner and outer fields and their interaction with each other. Cultivating qi through Qi Gong keeps you flexible through life's inevitable pulls and pushes. Cultivating qi through Qi Gong helps the organism to stay healthy and vital. Good energy is generated,

stagnant and exhausted energy expelled and the energy paths and gateways are kept unobstructed so that the qi can freely circulate.

Qi Gong can be used simply for staying healthy and helping to prevent disease, but its potential range is much wider and includes martial arts, inner alchemy and meditation. The practice contributes to mental awareness and calmness, emotional balance and spiritual sensitivity.

Qi Gong gives each practitioner a chance to take personal responsibility for their life-energy by learning how to deal with it. Qi Gong can be done by anyone, young or old, healthy, ill or disabled. It requires no equipment or special clothing and no previous experience. It can be done virtually anywhere. Most exercises are quite easy and soon give positive results.

Qi Gong can be used simply for staying healthy and helping to prevent disease, but its potential range is much wider and includes martial arts, inner alchemy and meditation. The practice contributes to mental awareness and calmness, emotional balance and spiritual sensitivity.

The average practitioner may spend a relatively short time exercising daily but it is possible to practise for long hours, doing certain exercises at specific times and in special surroundings. You could choose to pattern a whole life-style according to Qi Gong principles. There is indeed the ideal of the Taoist archetype, the Sage, who lives according to the Tao, who embodies the Tao. To witness today's Shaolin monks in their distinctive garments, their deft, flexible bodies performing astonishing and sometimes seemingly 'superhuman' acts is to experience the reality of the legendary adepts.

It's up to you to choose what you want from Qi Gong. You might want to keep healthy and fit or you might have to manage chronic illness. You could be a follower of the martial arts tradition, or have an interest in meditation and the deepening of spiritual awareness. Some practise Qi Gong with the intention of balancing the emotions. Even by entering in at one small corner, it is likely you will tune into the whole system of Qi Gong. This parallels the Taoist notion of an all-pervasive life-force whose Ground is everywhere.

Whichever variation you choose, you will encounter the fundamental principles of Qi Gong:

✦ it is possible to enhance, guide and cultivate life energy;

✦ you will return to a 'natural' state, or to that uncontaminated energetic core of being that pulses deeply within you.

Qi – Life Force

APPROACHING QI

Qi is energy. Qi is more than energy. Qi is life-force. Qi is the vital energy that is implicit in all life.
Qi has always been the key concept in Chinese medicine, myth, poetry and painting. The whole of manifestation
can be described in terms of qi. The reality and omnipresence of qi is so taken for granted in China that to
debate it would be as if a fish questioned the existence of water. Qi is omnipresent in descriptive common
language: one person has 'good' qi, another has 'tired' qi; someone of moral uprightness has 'bone' qi. A chef
can be complimented by reference to 'very good wok qi'; the weather in all its variations is called 'sky-qi'.

Qi is inside and outside of every living form. Qi governs the cosmic movement of the stars as well as each
minute fluctuation of breath in and out of our lungs. How can we define this concept, which occurs in so many
ways and on so many levels?

There is no definition of qi in the classical textbooks. For the Chinese, 'qi' requires no definition as it is
universally experienced. Furthermore, Chinese medicine is pragmatic and experiential. The emphasis is on how
qi works and what it does. How does qi work and what effect does it have? Chinese doctors can tell you about
your qi through evidence from pulses, tongue and skin texture, qualities of wetness, dryness, heat and cold in
the body and so on. Gifted Qi Gong healers are able to 'read' an energy field, noticing its strengths, deficiencies
and blockages. On a simple level you can investigate some manifestations of qi by looking inside yourself.

EXERCISE 1: EXPLORING QI

Close your eyes, look and feel inside. Notice what is happening in your body and mind: pulse, heartbeat, flow of breathing, peristaltic movements in the belly, the passing of thoughts and feelings, and other movements. Take your time, don't force anything. Just be aware ...

You perceived particular movements in yourself. There are many more. There is constant movement in all beings and phenomena throughout the entire universe.

Qi is seen as the activating force within all these movements – as electricity in a computer. Qi is the activating force and the movement itself. China's Sages said: life is movement; death is no movement; the difference between life and death is qi.

This moving force, qi, obeys observable laws and principles – including the great Law of Yin and Yang – which weave through life and apply to celestial, natural and human realms. A human being stands between Earth (Yin) and Heaven (Yang), the human offspring between cosmic Mother and Father, embedded within an interacting energy-field. As this energy-field is always in a process of change, the human has to adapt continuously. Resistance to movement and adaptation – resistance to change – prevents flow and brings sickness. One of the prominent functions of qi is constantly to re-balance this fluid energy-field. And qi needs to circulate freely through the body to do this work. Like air, qi can be stagnant, stale and unhealthy or fresh, free-moving and healthy. So now, in our initial exploration of qi, we have found the basic elements of movement, balance and flow.

The next key element for understanding qi is its transformative power, which is illustrated in a Chinese pictogram for 'qi' which shows rice, cooking and steaming. Rice (Yin) is cooked with fire (Yang) and produces steam (qi). The quantity of rice, the cooking water and the strength of the fire are balanced and measured in relation to each other. Rice can be over-cooked, under-cooked or of the right consistency. Poorly cooked rice can be a result of too much cooking water or too little; the fire can be applied too fiercely or turned off at the wrong moment. Qi arises when opposites are in harmonious mutual interaction. The true alchemy of fire, rice and water produces perfectly cooked rice, and this combination releases a distilled vapour, which is thought to contain the essence, energy and spirit of the rice. It is said that to steam vegetables in this vapour is to infuse them with the finest qi.

The manifold transformative functions of qi include all physiological processes like breathing, digestion and keeping the body warm. Through its functions qi keeps body processes like the blood circulation and all the organs in their natural order and dynamic relationship. If qi flows freely you are in good health.

Finally, qi actively protects by building a subtle shield around the body. This protecting shield filters noxious physical effects such as excess coldness or heat, strong winds and intrusive negative emotional energies from others.

PRE- AND POST-NATAL QI

Where does human qi come from? It is important here to discriminate between pre- and post-natal origins. The qi you receive before birth, mainly through inheritance from your parents is called pre-natal or inherited qi. The qi you acquire after birth, the qi you transform from food, water and air and the qi you receive directly from the universe is called post-natal or acquired qi. A synthesis of these energies – called normal or righteous qi – permeates the whole body.

Pre-natal qi

At the moment of conception, there is fusion of the parents' essence. This means that sperm and egg combine in an organic way to create essence qi, which contains a subtle blue-print of information for life, a coded package carrying the potentiality of the life to come.

Life demands energy from the battery as soon as the baby emerges from the womb.

The Taoists describe a more subtle and archetypal origin. Primal qi is originally created by Heaven and Earth and is 'transported' by the sexual union of the parents. The intensity of orgasmic union, the union of Yin and Yang, creates a vehicle that attracts cosmic energies to imprint primal qi into the new human-to-be. So the foetus is more than a product of genetic heritage. It is also influenced by qi received in the womb from the mother. This qi reflects the state of the mother, her physical and emotional health and attitude towards the unborn foetus.

The unique package of pre-natal qi cannot be changed. No one can alter genetic inheritance or circumstances of pregnancy and birth. On this level, each being comes into life with its pre-determined stock. Eventually, after severance of the umbilical cord, this package, this pre-natal essence, is stored in the body – in the kidneys, hormonal glands and sexual organs – constituting a basis of life force with particular strengths and weaknesses. Each individual being is unique.

Pre-natal qi can be seen as the given amount of energy in a battery. Life demands energy from the battery as soon as the baby emerges from the womb. From this perspective the quantity and quality of your qi is pre-determined and unalterable. Each person arrives into life with a particular personal amount of qi to spend throughout a finite time upon the earth. However, there is no need for fatalism – energy is also generated after birth.

Post-natal qi

After birth, energy is generated mainly through eating, drinking and breathing. Food qi is transformed through different refining stages in the digestive process. It is referred to as Yin qi since food and water come from the Earth. Breath qi, air qi, is transformed from breathing air. As it comes from Heaven it is referred to as Yang qi.

We also receive qi directly from the universe around us – whether we are aware of it or not. Sometimes the process is called 'qi breathing'. Qi Gong invites us to become more aware of this possibility and actively to use it.

The increase of energy is a core driving principle behind the practice of Qi Gong. Each individual is seen to have free will in the way the original store is handled.

All the post-natal qi we receive – be it through food, water, air or directly – can be seen as a gift from our cosmic parents, Mother Earth and Father Heaven, abundantly available to us all, as opposed to the limited package of pre-natal qi received from our actual parents. Whereas pre-natal qi diminishes as we get older, post-natal qi potentially compensates for this loss. Immortality may be the dream of some; most of us are probably content to maintain and cultivate our finite life energy through distinct practices and ways of life.

The principle of using post-natal qi to refill the battery can be likened to the Biblical story of the three sons who were given a quantity of talents by their father. One son buried his, another spent his, and the third invested his and increased the quantity. So it is that each individual has a choice with their precise stock of energy. It can be hidden, given away or increased.

The increase of energy is a core driving principle behind the practice of Qi Gong. Each individual is seen to have free will in the way the original store is handled. This free will is manifested primarily through choice of life-style, or attitude towards the changeable and unchangeable circumstances of life. Diet, learning to cope with emotions and stress, calming the mind, learning to adapt to change, breathing techniques and conscious sexual practice are all ways in which to handle and promote healthy energy management.

Qi gong is a practice of consciously and directly promoting the increase and cultivation of energy.

THE THREE TREASURES

On whatever level you begin to practise Qi Gong, there will be an impact on the whole body-energy-spirit system. The Chinese refer to this system and its interrelationship as The Three Treasures.

The Three Treasures – also referred to as jewels, flowers or the Taoist Trinity – are called jing (essence), qi (energy) and shen (spirit). It is common knowledge in China that health and longevity are directly determined by the strength, balance and cultivation of The Three Treasures. The Chinese perspective is like an embroidery, a spider's web representing a holistic model of the human being, showing specific links between levels of existence and indicating techniques for working within this intricate, interlaced system.

The Three Treasures can be differentiated for analytical purposes, but they form an indivisible whole. As it is written in the Wen Tze classic: *'The body is the temple of life. Energy is the force of spirit. Spirit is the governor of life. If one of them goes off balance, all three are damaged.'* Touch one and you touch them all.

There is a potential complication in these concepts. Qi is understood as universal life force, the cosmic energy of the universe. The differentiated qi is, together with jing and shen, only used concerning the human body, confirming to humanity its essence, energy and spirit. All three are manifestations of universal qi through different qualities, levels and densities.

Jing

Jing literally means essence, semen or sperm. It is the essence aspect of qi, the quintessence of human substance, the very basis of organic life.

Inborn jing is created by fusion of the parents' jing (sperm and egg) at conception and contains all genetic information defining individual constitution, special growth patterns and life span. Jing – in early pictograms written as 'germ' or 'grain' – is highly charged with potential: it is paralleled with the Early Sky of sunrise whereas qi is paralleled with the Full Sky: sun at its peak.

Generally, this means that jing is the foundation, the building blocks of the body. Specifically, jing is seen as a fluid-like essence/energy, located primarily in the sexual fluids, but also in lymph, lubricants surrounding joints, tears, sweat, urine and other body fluids. In this watery aspect, jing is a condensed form of qi: dark, silent, damp and warm.

The archetypal and energetic function of jing relates to sexuality. Jing has to do with sexuality, reproduction, the production of sperm, menstrual cycles and pregnancy. Jing attends to the continuation of the species. It is stored in the lower part of the body: kidneys, adrenal glands, sexual organs. In Qi Gong practice it is collected and cultivated in an area called the lower dan tian between navel and pubic bone, also known as the Lower Elixir Field.

As the roots of life, jing is also the very foundation of the body, providing the energetic material for an adequate growth of body and mind. In this function jing is included in long-term development, growth and decay. Further, it is responsible for the immune system and the capacity of the body to cope with accidents and illness. Recovery from sickness is clearly dependent on healthy jing.

Jing is lost as an inevitable consequence of ageing: to age means to lose jing. It is a rare old one who maintains an energy akin to the originally powerful presence of jing, when hormonal pulsation and the golden and elastic bloom of youth is at its most vivid. Joints stiffen, hair goes grey, skin becomes looser and the mind less agile.

Jing is especially lost through excessive sex in males; it is said that jing is spent with each ejaculation. For women it is lost through menstruation, pregnancy and menopause. A generally unhealthy life-style, including poor diet, ineffective breathing patterns, living in a polluted environment and experiencing continued emotional stress all claim their packets of jing.

Qi

Compared to jing, qi, as the second Treasure, is a more active and subtle aspect of energy. An activating and dynamic force, it is always moving. If jing were a light bulb, qi would be the electricity that makes it shine. Continuing this metaphor of the unlit light bulb, the organs, the whole body, could not work without the activating and moving force of qi.

While jing stands for slower and long-term developments, qi is connected with short-term cycles like breathing, digestion or any other physiological function. Qi activates, regulates, transforms and balances, holding the organism together in its dynamic processes. Through its regulating capacity it provides an adequate blood flow which nourishes all parts of the body. Qi is a regulating and transforming force in the jing-qi-shen system. For example, transforming food into food qi; food qi and breath qi into nutritive qi; nutritive and inborn qi into righteous qi.

The channels in which qi flows are called meridians. Acupuncture or acupressure mean putting a needle or finger pressure on a particular point of the meridian, thus regulating qi in a certain way. In Qi Gong there are exercises to manipulate qi through concentration on these meridians.

All organs are permeated by and surrounded by qi and each organ has its own characteristic qi. In diagnosis of disharmony, a Chinese doctor might comment on fiery heart qi, damp kidney qi or cold lung qi.

Shen

Shen most aptly translates as spirit, but in the Chinese system there is no separation of body and spirit. Shen resides in the body – in the heart – and has its own physical side. All Three Treasures are energy and matter. The Chinese – like modern physicists – do not sharply discriminate between matter and energy. Jing, qi and shen are all part of a matter-energy continuum, jing being positioned more at the substantial pole and shen more at the subtle pole.

An important third channel for the practise of inner Qi Gong, called chong mai, goes right through the middle of the body connecting crown and perineum. Travelling these pathways, in rest and stillness, activates the energy, balances it and brings the quietness and clarity of shen to the whole body-mind system.

Shen includes mind, intuition and spirit. As the mind aspect of spirit shen is the capacity to be aware and to think, to analyse, observe, discriminate and to interpret sensual perceptions or emotions. Strong shen enables fresh and clear insights, creative thinking, a more perceptive mind and well-balanced emotions. Shen manifests in distinct vibrations of the body and reflects in the light of the eyes. Called the 'Emperor residing in the heart', it is stored in the upper dan tian, in the Elixir Field between the eyebrows, and manifests itself in the world of meditation as well as in the world of the ego.

Shen flows through channels known as the Eight Extraordinary Meridians. Two of these feature in a classical Qi Gong exercise known as the Microcosmic Orbit (see page 98). Qi rises up the spine (du mai), and is moved down a middle line along the front of the body (ren mai). An important third channel for the practise of inner Qi Gong, called chong mai, goes right through the middle of the body connecting crown and perineum. Travelling these pathways, in rest and stillness, activates the energy, balances it and brings the quietness and clarity of shen to the whole body-mind system.

Shen – as spirit – represents silence and tranquillity. The cultivation of shen helps to turn the body-mind system away from constant activity, reaction and response, and into a place of peace and recuperation. This aspect of shen links humans with the cosmic Source.

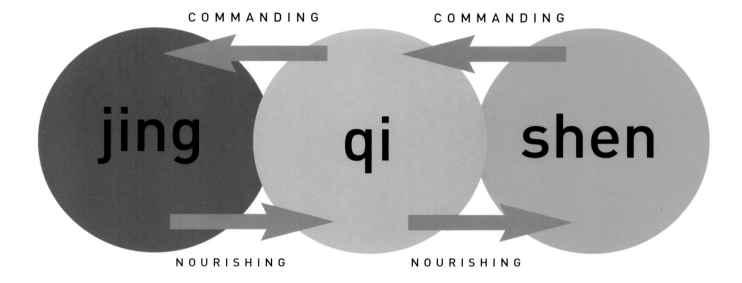

The nourishing and commanding lines: jing nourishes qi, which in turn nourishes shen, shen commands qi which commands jing.

JING, QI, SHEN

The Three Treasures, wrapped into one original unity before conception, start to differentiate as the individual begins to take form. Yet ideally they remain always linked in unity, functioning as a whole, supporting, influencing and balancing each other.

Jing is earthy, physical, sexual, Yin; shen is ethereal, fine, Yang, connecting humans with their cosmic Source. Qi is the middle force, linking, binding and balancing all. Just as the Yin-Yang symbol has a white dot in the black field and a black dot in the white field, jing has a spiritual component, and shen relates to matter. Shen is nourished by jing and qi; it needs the material base and energy. Shen is the flower, growing from roots and stem.

If you take care of your jing, your essential store of energy, and if you cultivate a good flow of qi, you have created the potential for the flowering of spirit. Once spirit has flowered, it can use its beauty in a return journey, leading qi, which then reinforces jing.

In Qi Gong, these three levels are all present. The flowering of shen – spiritual work, meditation – needs a strong foundation, a grounding in body awareness and emotional balance. Work on a qi and jing level – physical and energetic practice – is incomplete without the spark of shen.

In an ongoing natural process, jing is refined into qi and qi is refined into shen. This process is called the nourishing line. Jing nourishes qi and qi nourishes shen. Refinement and nourishment are supported by a certain life-style and by the practice of Qi Gong. At the same time, Qi Gong takes advantage of a different connecting principle of the Three Treasures – the commanding line. In this, shen commands qi and qi commands jing. Shen is the leader and guiding light for qi and jing, and it is through the quality of mental concentration, focus and visualization that qi is activated and commanded.

In other words, if you take care of your jing, your essential store of energy, and if you cultivate a good flow of qi, you have created the potential for the flowering of spirit. Once spirit has flowered, it can use its beauty in a return journey, leading qi, which then reinforces jing.

Qi Gong History

Imagine that you are looking at a silken scarf, on which are painted 44 figures, bending and moving before your eyes in the pleasure and innocence of playing with energy. Some stretch their arms high into the sky, others take low postures into the earth. Arms and legs move in graceful arcs and circles. The figures are young and old, male and female. If you were to imitate these movements, you would be practising Qi Gong. If you were to touch the silken material onto which each figure has been drawn you would enter history, streaming back 2,000 years through time.

This scarf was found 25 years ago by archaeologists excavating the tomb of King Ma of the Han dynasty (circa 200 BC) It was found half-soaked, folded, in a coffin. The discovery was named The Dao Yin.

As well as the illustrations, there are words. Movements and postures are given animal names such as bear, hawk, monkey, wolf; there is reference to medical conditions, such as arthritis or anxiety, as well as a description of the importance of breathing and of certain methods of practice.

The history of Qi Gong goes so far back in time that it is impossible to tell fact from fiction, reality from legend. The stories that linger carry the essence of Qi Gong. To follow the trail, imagine you are holding four strands plaited into a single ribbon in your hand. This ribbon represents Qi Gong now. Then let the strands loosen – three wind back to the long-distant past, to shamanism, early Chinese medicine and the monasteries. One takes us to more modern times.

THE SHAMANIC HERITAGE

In many parts of the world, shamans were probably the earliest practitioners of healing and energy-work. As health and sickness were seen in relationship to the powers and energies of nature and the 'other world', shamans travelled outside their bodies in order to find a harmonious balance with these energies.

In the 'other' world, the shaman no longer operates from a daylight plane of the everyday, familiar world. He – or particularly in old China, she – comes into direct communication with plants, animals, cosmic energies and discarnate beings of benevolent and malevolent dispositions, travelling deep into the Earth or high into Heaven, moving with animals or riding on birds, moving as animals, flying as birds.

The shaman enters a state of trance through fasting, singing, ecstatic dancing and sometimes taking natural hallucinogens. In this way, normal social controls of body movements and expression are by-passed, as different energies penetrate the shaman's body and consciousness, resulting in trembling, shaking, guttural and high-pitched animal and bird sounds, talking in secret languages and dancing movements sometimes intensified by drumming and shaking rattles.

In their work, shamans find power through alliance with auxiliary energies, especially animal energies. In this alliance they share – as Eliade writes – 'the secrets of Life and Nature, the secrets of longevity and immortality'.

In all cultures, the shaman's healing techniques include energy-work: drawing, or literally sucking out sick energy or demons, giving the patient a fresh and clear infusion of energy. Qi Gong healers in past and present time engage in similar activities: diagnosing energetic imbalance in the body, re-balancing such disturbance by transferring qi, activating the qi flow in the patient and removing congested or bad qi.

The shaman is not only healer or 'energy worker': his or her role in the tribe or community is that of mediator between the visible and invisible worlds and includes rain-making, aiding the fertility of crops and protecting the tribe against pestilence or aggressors. Enclosed in this mediation between the visible and invisible worlds, embedded in forms and postures of ritual activity, we may detect the primordial origins of Qi Gong: in the work of the spirit, prayers to Heaven and Earth and their representative Gods; in the work of the body, exercises to cope with elemental forces and catastrophes, or severe changes in climate. In the time of Emperor Yao, the land was devastated by a big flood and consequent large-scale residue of stagnant water. Remedies were sought for the obstructed waterways – and for the people whose health was undermined by the damage and pollution. Breathing and moving exercises were seen as parallel to the rescue of the affected countryside.

In their work, shamans find power through alliance with auxiliary energies, especially animal energies. In this alliance they share – as Eliade writes – 'the secrets of Life and Nature, the secrets of longevity and immortality'.

The profound experience for the shaman is not to act as if he or she was the animal, but to become the animal. This can lead into an ecstasy of communion with natural and cosmic rhythms. We find here one of the origins of Qi Gong in the form of animal dances. In the Zhou dynasty shamans used to perform exorcism-like rituals. In this ritual shamans in bearskins and villagers wearing masks of animals such as dragons, horses and tigers, would dance to ward off pestilence and demons.

From a later dynasty, Prince Wang created a crane dance, promising immortality, and was said to have approached Heaven on the back of a crane. According to legends the Yellow Emperor and a substantial entourage were transported to Heaven by a bearded dragon!

Early Chinese history is rich with stories of the ecstasy of flying. An Emperor, Shun, had the magical capacity of flight, revealed to him by women. Magical capacities were needed not only by the shaman or healer, but also by Emperors, as magical ability, mastery of nature was equivalent to authority. From a later dynasty, Prince Wang created a crane dance, promising immortality, and was said to have approached Heaven on the back of a crane. According to legend, the Yellow Emperor and a substantial entourage were transported to Heaven by a bearded dragon! These stories read as metaphors for transcendence. Cranes, known in China as the patriarchs of the feathered tribe, were seen especially as intermediaries between Heaven and Earth, and symbolized immortality and longevity.

Preoccupation with animals has been retained in the Qi Gong tradition. It ranges from a recommendation by Chuang Tzu, a famous Taoist philosopher and pupil of Lao Tzu, to move like a bear and stretch like a bird, to the development of a complex form, the 'Five Animal Frolics'. This movement sequence is connected to Hua

Tuo, a doctor living around 200AD. He tried to understand how tiger, deer, bear, monkey and crane use their energy, and 'translated' their essential energies into human movement patterns.

The Five Animal Frolics is said to be the basis of all martial arts and is alive and transmitted in our time through many variations. Nowadays, the Five Animal Frolics, the Wild Goose and Crane Qi Gong forms are the most popular forms and remind us, in their more spontaneous and cathartic aspects, of shamanic rituals.

On a still deeper level, practitioners connect with a longing to be back in a primordial, natural space, speaking a language of nature, being one with nature.

Qi Gong practitioners training in animal forms gradually acquire the skills attributed to particular animals: balance, suppleness, grace and strength. Animal movements can even be practised with specific emphasis. Michael Tse suggests that to raise the arms above the head like the horns of a deer stimulates the qi circulation of the liver; to stretch the arms like a bird spreading its wings is good for the heart and for relieving tension; rubbing and slapping the body and moving like a monkey is good for the spleen; stretching the arms out in front while breathing out, like a tiger, is good for releasing tension in the lungs, and bending forward like the bear is good for the back and kidneys.

On a still deeper level, practitioners connect with a longing to be back in a primordial, natural space, speaking a language of nature, being one with nature. Ghosts of shaman ancestors emerge from ancient memories into the present, as the Qi Gong pupil – who might not even know of their existence – shapes arms gently into wings, sends tree roots deep into the ground through the soles of the feet, and acts as a unifying channel for the forces of Yin and Yang, Earth and Heaven, to meet through a longing and receptive body.

EARLY CHINESE MEDICINE

If you now follow the direction of the second ribbon, you might chance upon a dialogue, 4,000 years ago. The Yellow Emperor asked his minister Ch'i Po why peoples in ancient times attained the age of 100, staying active and not deteriorating, whereas people of his time reached only half that age and became decrepit. Ch'i Po answered that 'in ancient times, people understood Tao, patterned themselves upon the Yin and the Yang and lived in harmony'.

The 'ancient times' refers to a mythical Golden Age, a Chinese Garden of Eden, where people lived in the Tao, without splitting man and nature, mind and body. The Sages of Chinese history embodied this Golden Age, living in simplicity and according to the laws of nature and the unity of body and soul. Ch'i Po went on to describe their temperance in eating and drinking; they rose and retired at regular hours; controlled spirit and passion in order not to exhaust vital forces; cultivated tranquillity and accepted life under any conditions.

The wise physician, and indeed the wise patient, cures diseases before they develop. Cultivating qi, clearing the system of noxious effects, freeing blockages so that qi can flow, allows qi to take care of you.

This discussion about longevity and life in harmony with the Tao initiated China's first medical book, the bible of Chinese medicine, *The Yellow Emperor's Classic on Internal Medicine*. It is attributed to the Yellow Emperor, although historians date this book at around the second or third century BC and consider the Yellow Emperor to be a legendary rather than historical figure. In this classic text, the emphasis is on prevention. The wise physician, and indeed the wise patient, cures diseases before they develop. Cultivating qi, clearing the system of noxious effects, freeing blockages so that qi can flow, allows qi to take care of you. A long and healthy life is possible. The Yellow Emperor's techniques for prevention are implicit in present-day Qi Gong. Shamanic healing dances gradually gave way to more specific practices: breathing exercises, slow movements that keep the qi flow unobstructed and techniques for controlling mind, emotions and sexuality.

The focus slowly moved away from the shaman or a healer as the ultimate authority, to taking personal responsibility for energetic health and well-being. This attitude of responsibility, which started with early Qi Gong, carries a modern resonance. Now, as then, people want to have good health and live long. Now, as then, some people want to live forever! The practitioners associated with immortality in early Chinese history were the alchemists.

If you look at alchemy as the process of transformation, alchemical happenings occur in daily life all around you. Water turns into steam, or into ice; heavy objects can be melted down. Throughout the ages, those who longed for more spectacular transformation approached the alchemists, intent upon finding the pill that would grant youth and immortality; searching for the catalyst that could turn lead into gold.

The cultivation of Yang, symbolizing Heaven, and Yin symbolizing Earth, happens through inner processes of breathing, movement, sexual yoga, visualization, cultivation and transformation of qi.

In China Wai Dan is the name for Outer Alchemy: practitioners of which explored the potential of herbs and minerals in the quest for elixirs of immortality. Ambitious noble men paid for their immortal longings with sudden death when the pills and potions they trustingly digested turned out to be toxic!

In the second century Wei Po Yang wrote the first known treatise on alchemy, using esoteric language. Called *The Kinship of The Three*, it referred to spiritual, human and natural realms. Some interpreted it literally as a book of outer, material recipes; for those who understood, Wei Po initiated the lineage of Nei Dan or Inner Alchemy. The human body is itself the alchemist's alembic or cooking bowl; the body is its own transformative container. The cultivation of Yang, symbolizing Heaven, and Yin symbolizing Earth, happens through inner processes of breathing, movement, sexual yoga, visualization, cultivation and transformation of qi.

Again we see that the emphasis shifts from magical work to self-help. If there is reliance on outer forms, you ask for the shaman's wizardry, the alchemist's pill, and nowadays designer pills and creams to keep us young and lovely. If you turn inwards, you look at the transformative possibility of inner work.

A notable figure called Ko Hung, also known as the Master who Embraces Simplicity, took the expression of Nei Dan further. A man endowed with universal knowledge, he was also a pathologist and a general. In keeping with the essence of Taoism, he withdrew from the busy world, retiring eventually to the mountains where he died, aged 81, sitting in meditation, his body still extraordinarily young in appearance.

27

Ko Hung discarded the search for physical immortality through the superstitious elements of Wai Dan. His understanding created a clearer distinction between the quest for good health and a long life, and spiritual immortality.

This differentiation contains the two-fold essence of Qi Gong practice.

✦ Qi Gong as a health-enhancing discipline, self-generated, amplified by the qi field of nature and /or a Qi Gong master or healer.

✦ Qi Gong as meditation, the art of cultivating tranquillity and peace of mind, and re-establishing contact with Oneness.

THE MONASTIC TRADITION

The final ribbon of the past leads us to Buddhist and Taoist monasteries. Inner Alchemy brought with it the meditative and spiritual aspect of Qi Gong.

'Don't listen with the ears; listen with the mind. No, don't listen with the mind, but listen with the qi … This qi is an emptiness which is receptive to all things. The Tao is understood through emptiness, Emptiness is the fasting of the mind.'

Chuang Tzu points us away from distractions of the senses, taking us step by step into quietness and emptiness.

There is a tradition of Taoist seekers in search of simplicity, naturalness and emptiness, in search of quietness of mind, moving to mountains and riverbanks, to meditate and live alone. Like the Indian Yogi, the Taoist fled the world of dust, to live life according to the Tao. Yoga is probably older than Qi Gong and Yogic techniques – along with Buddhist scriptures – were brought to China from India by early pilgrims and Buddhist monks 2,000 years ago.

A key figure of this time, pictured bulging-eyed and ferocious, is the legendary Bodhidarma. An Indian monk, son of a South Indian Brahmin, he left his home south of Madras heading for China, bringing Buddhist scriptures, Yoga, pranayama breathing and movement from an Indian martial art.

Bodhidarma travelled north, crossing the Yangtse river on a reed, finally arriving at the Shaolin Monastery. Discovering that the monks were in poor physical shape, having been engaged only in mental and meditative activities, he taught them that meditation should be based on the foundation of a strong and vibrant body. The monks began to learn breathing techniques and movement forms, which became the basis of meditation practice as well as a fundamental martial art – the birthing hour of the famous Shaolin hard Qi Gong and Kung fu.

Qi Gong in the Shaolin Monastery demonstrates a visible polarity of stillness and movement. The body is perfectly tuned; the mind, focused and one-pointed, creates an impenetrable protective shield and a core centre of quietness and concentration. The training is not primarily for fighting purposes. Body-mind discipline is maintained as part of a spiritual way of life.

The lineage of monastery Qi Gong is characterized by secrecy. The master would teach a small number of pupils, waiting for a long time until accepting someone worthy of receiving the lineage. Teaching very slowly, he would only gradually reveal his knowledge. The Qi Gong transmitted in the monasteries, as well as the Qi Gong transmitted in family clans would only be open to a very small number of people. A high standard of training was maintained, but Qi Gong developed an elitist character.

In the monasteries, as well as in family clans the teaching passed on almost exclusively to men. In family clans there was always the risk that women would pass on secrets once they left their family walls for marriage into another clan.

MODERN TIMES

We are now taking a giant leap, via our last ribbon, to the 20th century where we find the Chinese communists ambivalent to Qi Gong and Chinese medicine. Prior to the Communist take-over, the Guoming dan government wanted to replace Chinese medicine entirely with Western medicine. Mao Zedong, however, ordered a review of the 'Storehouse of Treasures' – as he called Chinese medicine – to see what could be made generally available to the 'masses', to investigate scientifically its effects, to clear the whole system of ideological 'impurity' and to put together the best of both Chinese and Western medical systems.

The practice of Qi Gong – at least in a reduced form – was continued. There were even two sanatoriums in the mid 1950s specializing in Qi Gong cures, training centres for Qi Gong teachers and, in 1959, a conference on Qi Gong sponsored by the Ministry of Public Health.

There were Qi Gong healers and teachers in hospitals and sanatoriums; Qi Gong was taught to students, athletes and soldiers to improve their capacities. It is rumoured that certain Communist leaders were treated by the best Qi Gong healers.

At the same time, Qi Gong as an offspring of Taoism was deeply mistrusted, seen as superstitious, religious, elitist and counter-revolutionary. Taoism, with its emphasis on individual responsibility, its disregard for formal values and norms, its sometimes anarchic and eccentric features seemed individualistic, dangerous for a totalitarian system. Consequently Qi Gong was stripped of its spiritual and philosophical garb, cut off from its Taoist roots and reshaped as an effective and neutral 'tool'. It was reduced to a physical and mental level, researched, systematized and standardized. Meditative and holistic aspects were discarded.

This manoeuvre was not only motivated by ideological arguments. There was a wish to simplify and standardize Qi Gong in order to make it generally available, to remove it from small, elitist schools and use it in a more pragmatic way for public health. There were Qi Gong healers and teachers in hospitals and sanatoriums; Qi Gong was taught to students, athletes and soldiers to improve their capacities. It is rumoured that certain Communist leaders were treated by the best Qi Gong healers. Effort in the field of research brought Qi Gong into the realm of 'science' – but its less measurable, more intangible and poetic Way was still banned under the grip of the prevailing ideology.

The eruption of the Cultural Revolution in the 1960s meant the cessation of Qi Gong altogether. Even the hope of its surviving as 'medical Qi Gong' was destroyed. Qi Gong was made illegal, teachers were persecuted, imprisoned and 're-educated'. The methods of repression were excessively harsh; many teachers were killed. Qi Gong disappeared from the public field. It went underground.

After ten years of Cultural Revolution, as China came out of this experience into chaos, Qi Gong started to emerge slowly throughout the battered country. As in so many periods throughout history, change brought favour where there had been disfavour. Growing pride began to accompany the research into the effectiveness of 'official' medical Qi Gong. Along with acupuncture, these practices were seen as treasures of Chinese medicine. In the 1980s, scientifically sophisticated research was carried out into the effects of external Qi Gong and brought information about 'superhuman' abilities and 'new' powerful energies. Beijing hosted the first conference of the World Scientific Association of Medical Qi Gong in 1979. In 1985 the Chinese Qi Gong Science Association was founded. In 1987, university courses in Qi Gong were instituted.

The re-emergence of Qi Gong was spectacular. A conservative estimate suggests that 300 styles are currently in circulation; a more extravagant claim puts the number at 4,000!

At the same time, the other aspect of Qi Gong, the meditative and the spiritual, was pushing through like bright blades of grass where it had been trodden under. The re-emerging Taoist essence began to breathe again after having been stifled under the communists and savaged by the Cultural Revolution.

The re-emergence of Qi Gong was spectacular. A conservative estimate suggests that 300 styles are currently in circulation; a more extravagant claim puts the number at 4,000!

Many of these forms were newly created, or re-fashioned from old forms. There were more people practising Qi Gong than ever before in history. While official 'medical Qi Gong' developed as a major instrument of Public Health, the 'new' Qi Gong was practised in parks and private houses rather than in institutions. It grew from the grass-roots rather than from scientific or academic research.

Often stories would emerge of people suffering from severe diseases curing themselves and finding insight into healing mechanisms, which could then be taught to others. This is the tale of Zhao Jin Xiang, creator of the modern Crane Qi Gong. He was born in 1934 in a little village and suffered from tuberculosis and pleurisy. He moved to Beijing to a sanatorium, but his condition steadily worsened. He had already lost grandparents and a brother because the doctors were unable to help the family. So he decided to try and heal himself. He studied medical and Taoist books, practised inner Qi Gong and meditation. His condition slowly improved. When he had healed, he had also changed personally. He was determined to help others. On his way home from the sanatorium, he travelled in the same train compartment as a Qi Gong master. The master showed him a sequence of exercises. After practising these, Zhao Jin Xiang felt light as a bird. From this experience, he created a form combining stillness, formal and spontaneous movements. This is the Crane Qi Gong form.

In a curious parallel this and other similar stories reflect a pattern from the shamanic tradition. A shaman-to-be is often involved in a serious personal crisis: either severe sickness, mental disorder or a self-chosen hardship connected with the vision quest.

A further echo of shamanism is present in the erratic, uncontrolled, jerky movements and emotional cathartic sounds of spontaneous Qi Gong: a form that is now erupting into popularity in contrast to the more uniform movements of the Beijing tai ji style.

Seen in a socio-political context, the new Qi Gong is a form of liberation after years of the suppression of individuality and the imposition of ideological standards. Qi Gong, though, is surely not a political movement. Its revolutionary character can be seen rather in its autonomous concentration of the body-mind; in its trust of the inner experience rather than following orders from the outside.

The partial banning of Qi Gong in recent history, and the Falun Gong affair, show us that although Qi Gong itself is not political, it becomes a political issue when it is seen as threatening the communist system and its values. Perhaps the substantial increase in meditative Qi Gong, which we observe alongside the rise of spontaneous Qi Gong, is an even bigger threat. Communism – after all – has failed to sever the roots of Taoist culture; there is an intense hunger for spiritual food.

Finally, and in contrast to early times of exclusive secrecy, Qi Gong is no longer restricted to China; books, teachers and practitioners are streaming out all over the world.

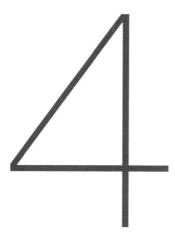

Ingredients for Practice

Beginning Qi Gong is like learning to drive. Eventually, with practice and familiarity, the art of driving becomes second nature. Clutch, break and accelerator, steering wheel and indicator are manipulated with almost thoughtless ease. However, the first few experiences, with a large L-plate attached to the car, consist of learning distinctly and separately each mechanical function.

In Qi Gong, you learn about the different ingredients, knowing that they all become part of one inseparable whole. The ingredients of Qi Gong influence and are influenced by each other.

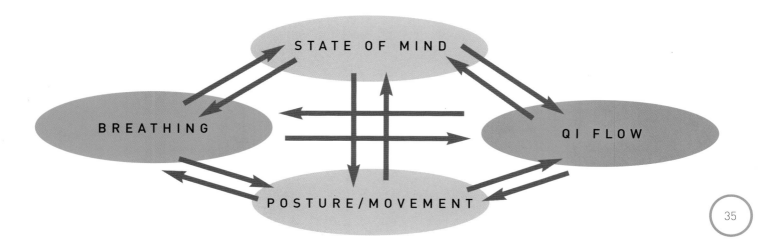

A quiet and peaceful state of mind induces slow and restful breathing; even, continuous breathing steadies the mind; standing with feet well planted, body balanced and head lightly resting on the shoulders, increases energy-flow, encourages even breathing and quiets the mind ... It's a pleasant activity – almost a meditation – to continue connecting all the possibilities of this interactive diagram.

Qi Gong is not a performance. It is about becoming aware of yourself through exercise. Practice is a balance of following instructions, and yet remaining spontaneous, open and aware of effects. This particular perspective is amplified later in The Tao of Practice (see page 77).

TIME AND PLACE OF PRACTICE

Qi Gong can be practised anywhere and at any time of the day or night. On the other hand, for expert practitioners or for those who follow Qi Gong as a way of life, there is an encyclopaedic amount of detail about when and where to practise for maximum benefit. Ideally, you practise at dawn in natural surroundings which include trees and water. You wear loose clothing made of natural fibre so that you can move and breathe comfortably. You are either barefoot or wearing shoes with thin soles, allowing contact with the earth – think again of Chinese practitioners in loose cotton clothes and soft tai ji shoes moving slowly and quietly in the local park under early morning trees, or near water.

The most obvious reason for practising early in the morning is that you are not yet in gear with your daily routine. You can create an unobstructed free space after rising to enjoy the special fresh atmosphere of the early morning – starting your day in a relaxed and energetic way. The time from midnight to noon is called 'the time of the living breath' – newly waking up nature breathing with you in support of your practice. The time around sunrise corresponds to spring, where you plant the seed for your day.

Times of changes – around sunrise when Yin (night) gives way to Yang (day), or at sunset when Yang gives way to Yin – are seen as the most potent periods for practice. In general, the second choice for practice is late afternoon or early evening after you have completed your day's work.

If you want to exercise specifically to strengthen or heal a certain organ of the body, you have to choose the time from the meridian time-table. According to Chinese Medicine, qi influences each different organ in turn in a two-hourly cycle.

Meridian Time-table

1	**Gallbladder**	11pm–1am
2	**Liver**	1am–3am
3	**Lung**	3am–5am
4	**Large Intestine**	5am–7am
5	**Stomach**	7am–9am
6	**Spleen**	9am–11am
7	**Heart**	11am–1pm
8	**Small Intestine**	1pm–3pm
9	**Bladder**	3pm–5pm
10	**Kidney**	5pm–7pm
11	**Pericardium**	7pm–9pm
12	**Triple Burner**	9pm–11pm

It is neither advisable nor necessary to keep to this specialized time-table as a beginner. If you should need exercises for particular organs, or for healing, you should consult a doctor or expert Qi Gong teacher.

CAUTION

Whatever time you choose for your practice, there are certain rules to keep in mind:

✦ Don't practise right after a meal, leave one hour at least before starting. It is also unwise to practise if you are very hungry.

✦ Don't practise in the middle of ongoing intense physical or mental work. Try to end your working business first or at least make a clear and distinct break.

✦ Don't practise when you are exhausted or sick. When nervous, upset or in an unstable mood, calm down first, or if this doesn't work, leave your practice for another time.

A good idea is to include Qi Gong in your daily schedule: to practise at about the same time each day. Your body-mind becomes conditioned and then begins to want the experience, just as you automatically clear the night-feeling from your mouth by cleaning your teeth in the morning. If you can, practise in natural surroundings. Being in the midst of trees or green supports your qi. As you stand by a tree, you too can send your roots deep into the earth, hold your stance strong and upright and move your arms freely in the air like branches in the wind. Flowing water nearby enhances the sensation of the qi flow inside you.

These are the requirements for a good practice space:

✦ Either practise in nature or in a quiet room. Some people practising indoors choose music or recordings of natural sounds to create a background atmosphere.

✦ You need fresh air, but not too much wind. Cold wind is especially harmful in the early morning when the energy system is still waking up.

✦ You need warmth, but not excess heat or full sun.

You might wish to create a special place, perhaps even arranging objects such as candles, flowers, a picture or sacred statue. Even if you have no option but to practise in the most unsuitable surroundings, you can virtually transform them: use your imagination as if you had an inner screen, and visualize a beautiful place, creating an interior space that allows you to practise in the middle of even the most noisy and polluted external circumstances.

WARM-UP

In the morning, it is best to wake up to yourself with gentle exercises that bring you to body awareness, and then to move on to more strenuous practice. Starting with lively exercises and ending quietly is better for practice at the end of the day.

Our warm-up exercise is for the start or the end of the day. It tunes the body and concentrates the mind on exercising, shakes off tension and early-morning tiredness or the exhaustion of the later part of the day.

Most of the exercises suggested in the following sequence are taken from self-massage techniques, which are effective for bringing you into body awareness and awakening your qi streams.

EXERCISE 2: WARM-UP SEQUENCE

1 Stand with feet shoulder-width apart, toes pointing forward, knees relaxed and soft, slightly bent. Place your hands on the area beneath your navel (dan tian) palm over palm. Breathe into your belly. Focus on your dan tian and your breath for a while.

2 Massage your hands and wrists as if you were vigorously washing them, then rub the palms briskly together.

3 Stroke your face firmly several times as if you were washing it.

4 Using your middle fingers follow the lines firmly from the corners of the mouth, past the sides of the nose, between the eyebrows and up the forehead until the hairline and back, several times.

1

2

3

4

5 With middle fingers – firmly but not painfully – make circles in opposite directions around each eye. Change direction after some time.

6 Comb firmly through your hair from the front to the back with fingertips or fingernails, down to the base of the skull.

7 Pat the head firmly and gently with open hands or with your fingertips.

8 Stroke firmly over the head, imagining that you are removing tension and tired qi, shaking the fingers afterwards as if to free them from the tired energy.

5

6

8

9   Massage your ears inside and out.

10 Rub your hands up and down the temples.

11 Stroke the base of the skull, by moving the fingers horizontally towards and away from each other.

12 Raise the right arm and bring the fingers of the right hand to the neck. Create slight tension by pushing the right elbow back as far as it will comfortably go. Massage the neck and between the shoulder blades. Alternate with the left arm.

13 Circle your shoulders, letting the arms hang freely, first rolling forwards and then backwards.

14 Putting your hands on your hips, circle the hips to the right and then to the left, several times.

15 Keeping your feet well-planted and moving the waist, allow the arms to swing freely around the body. Left arm slaps over the right shoulder as the back of the right hand hits the lower back, palm outward.

9

10

11

12

13

Turn the waist so that the right arm slaps over the left shoulder as the back of the left hand hits the lower back, palm outwards. Continue this exercise and the next two as long as you want.

16 Keep the waist moving. Clasp your hands loosely into fists. The right fist swings to hit just below the left collarbone; the left fist hits the lower back with the fist outwards; the left fist swings to hit just below the right collarbone, the outer side of the right fist hits the lower back.

17 Continuing with the waist swing, gently slap just under your navel with loosely folded fist, the other hand, still in the loose fist, slapping the lower back.

18 Pat your left arm from the outer hand up to the shoulder, and from the shoulder along the inside of the arm down to the palm. Repeat several times. Firmly stroke the tensions and tiredness downwards and outwards, including the shoulder, arm and fingers. Then pull at the fingertips as if you are removing loose threads. Change to the other side, with the left hand patting the right arm.

14

15

16

17

19 Raise your left arm. Pat the left side of the body with the right hand from the underarm to the waist. Then stroke firmly downwards. Change to the other side.

20 Let your head hang down, lower your back. Slap your lower back with the palms of your hands. Slowly unfold and raise the back, lifting the head last until you are upright again. Rub your lower back gently.

21 Bend down once more. With both hands, slap the inside and outside of the left leg from thigh to ankle several times. Then the right. Slowly raise the back.

22 Put your right hand on your navel, and your left hand on your lower back, opposite the navel. Stroke firmly down the left leg, right hand in front, left hand behind. Move upwards again, then reverse the position of the hands by gently massaging your waist, bringing the right hand around to the back and the left to the front. Then move down the right leg, left hand in front and right hand on the back. Change direction again by massaging halfway with each hand around the waist. Repeat several times.

18   18   19   20   21

23 Bring both hands to your knees. Bend your knees, circle to the left and to the right, several times.

24 Standing upright once more, put your hands on your hips. Lift the left foot to a comfortable height. Kick out with your toes straight, then kick out pushing your heel to the front. Circle the foot by rotating the ankle to the left three times and then to the right three times. Repeat with the right foot.

25 Put both hands on your dan tian. Concentrate for some time on your breath and on the dan tian. Quietly collect the energy.

In addition to the warm-up sequence – or instead of it – you could do a popular cleaning routine. By shaking in a particular way, you clear the body internally, and make it receptive for new and fresh energy.

22

23

24

24

25

EXERCISE 3: THE RETURN OF SPRING (SHAKING EXERCISE)

✦ Stand with your feet well-planted, shoulder-width apart and parallel on the floor, toes pointing to the front. Your eyes are slightly open, looking forward. Your knees are relaxed, and the body upright.

✦ Initiate a gentle bouncing movement from your knees. This bouncing movement, like a wave, originates exclusively from the knees. Keep the whole body and particularly the shoulders loose. The arms also hang loosely, not moving intentionally, but moving passively with the bouncing. Loosen your head and neck. Don't control the breathing: just let it happen.

✦ Imagine your meridians as a system of energy-channels in the body. It is not necessary to imagine an accurate picture, but rather to hold a sense of an energy-network in your body. The obstacles that may block the flow of energy in some parts of the system are shaken loose and move downwards through the body, deep into the ground. While you're bouncing, keep your feet flat on the floor.

THE QI GONG STATE

To practise Qi Gong you have to come into – and stay in – a special state of mind. This is called 'The Qi Gong State' or ru jing, and in it the spirit becomes still. Stillness is a relative concept; life is movement and there is always movement; the mind is never still. The Qi Gong state includes a relative stillness of mind, or a state of not being identified with perceptions and thoughts.

The process of dis-identification is referred to by Li Zhi-Chang as cutting off the six roots: eyes, ears, nose, tongue, body, imagination. As these roots, which normally take you out into participation with the external world, become weaker, the inner focus becomes more intense. For example you might see someone walking past. Normally your eyes would grasp the image and your mind and imagination might become busy with what to do or say and you would send energy out into the world. If you had temporarily cut this root, the image would pass, be noticed, without involvement or action, and the energy would be maintained for inner work.

Initially it is not easy for a beginner to come into and abide in this state. Useful methods that help are relaxation techniques, working with the breath and meditative self-inquiry. We will look at breathing later in the chapter. In this section we concentrate on relaxation and inner focus.

Relaxation

Relaxation of the body is essential: without a relaxed body, the breath can't become calm, the mind can't become relaxed and still. Observe any cat! Their relaxation is not to do with drowsiness, but it is restful. It is an alertness that does not cause tension. It is an active relaxation. Master Li compares the effects of relaxation with giving water to a thirsty plant. Beginners especially should give significant time to this preparatory step.

EXERCISE 4: RELAXATION ALONG FOUR LINES

Sit comfortably on a chair, back straight but not stiff. Concentrate on your dan tian, watch your breath and let it become calm.

1   Take your awareness to the crown of your head and after a while allow the awareness to move down over your face. As this happens, relax your forehead, eyebrows, eyes, cheekbones, cheeks, nose, lips and jaw muscles. Let the awareness continue to move down over the surface of the throat and down to your chest. Feel the chest moving as you breathe. Go down to the belly. Feel the belly moving as you breathe. Relax down the front of the thighs, knees, shin-bone and upper part of the feet. Focus on your big toes, imagining them filled with energy.

2   After some time, return to the crown. Now move down the back line, initially relaxing the back of the head and neck. Put your awareness between the shoulder blades and relax the upper back. Go down to the lower back and relax in this area. Move over your buttocks to the back of the thighs, relaxing; relax the back of the knees, the calves, heels and soles of the feet. End this line by concentrating on the small toes.

3   After some time, return to the crown. This time, follow the two side-lines. Concentrate on your temples and ears, and then move down the side-lines of your throat to your shoulders.

Relax your shoulders, letting them sink down. Relax your upper arms, elbows, lower arms, wrists, hands and fingers. Concentrate energy on the two middle fingers for a while. Then lift your shoulders a little with the in-breath and as they slowly sink down again let your awareness move down the sides of the torso, over the hips, along the inner and outer sides of the legs and knees down to the ankles. Move your awareness along the inner and outer edges of the feet. Finally concentrate on your fourth toes.

4   After some time, return to the crown. Imagine now that you move down a middle line through the very centre of your body, concentrating on the middle of the brain, and from there loosening and relaxing any tension. If you feel particularly tense in this area, imagine ironing out knots and creases. Move down further through the middle of your head, the inside of your mouth and throat, melting all tensions. Move along the middle line of your chest cavity, relaxing, move along the middle line of your belly, relaxing from the inside out. Then let your pelvic floor sink down, as you sit fully on the chair. Move down through the inner lines of your legs, loosening your muscles from there, moving then to the centre of your knees, through to the middle line of your lower legs and moving right through to the feet. Concentrate for a while on the soles of your feet.

Once you are used to this way of relaxation, imagine four waves going down the body one by one – or even all at the same time. It's like taking a relaxation shower.

Meditative Self-Inquiry

This is a meeting between Qi Gong and meditation. Use it as preparation – or as an exercise in its own right.

5

EXERCISE 5: MEDITATIVE SELF-INQUIRY

Sit on a chair or a cushion. Close your eyes, watch your breath and calm down. After a while start scanning your inner body with a calm and neutral gaze. You are looking at your body, energy, thoughts and feelings in a non-judgemental, gentle and unforced way. You are aware of your body just as it is. Cultivate this acceptance even if there are tensions, grumbles and confusion. Observe your sensations, your feelings, your thoughts. Be aware of your state now in the present. Be very accepting of it. Be aware of the relaxation needs of your body. Adapt to these needs by allowing tiny inner changes like relaxing, breathing into tense places, melting tightness. Let yourself be guided. Take as long as you like.

In the beginning, acquiring the Qi Gong state takes time, and needs formal exercises for entry. Eventually, your body and energy become familiar with the state and can more easily be triggered into it. With familiarity, body relaxation, breathing activities and mental stillness are no longer separate processes but happen simultaneously.

POSTURE

Sitting, standing or moving are everyday activities, which usually happen without thought. In Qi Gong, it is essential to re-learn or re-organize how you sit, stand or move, as the effectiveness of an exercise depends on the correct posture or movement. Re-learning in this way, and learning the exercises can be hard work for beginners. There are many details to remember, and there is the added paradox of having to do it in a natural and relaxed way.

A teacher, giving an example and correcting you, a mirror or a video, helpfully feed back from the outside how your posture looks. The fine-tuning of the posture is done inside by gently adjusting, relaxing, focusing on the centre-point of gravity, until the balance feels right. Eventually, a meeting of outer physical adjustment and inner fine-tuning brings the required position or movement. Ultimately, the right posture is found and experienced inside, and projected outside.

Ideally a posture is natural and easy. It is not forced by will power and/or tension, but sustained by qi power. For example, you might be doing a sitting exercise and having difficulty holding the back in an upright position. If you hold this position only by tension, the flow of qi is inhibited and you need too much energy and concentration of the mind to stay upright. A better way would be to lean your back against support until you naturally want to bring yourself into the upright position.

Ideally a posture is relaxed and stable. This might sound like a contradiction but it simply means that you don't use more energy than necessary. Observe the stance of people around you! You'll notice that some use too much energy to stand. They probably have weak legs and/or they mistrust the holding quality of the ground. Trying to compensate, they use will-power and muscles. This state, called 'over-grounded' in body-psychotherapy, is characteristically rigid and inflexible. To find a more organic stance, the tension in the muscles has to melt. Relaxation is needed so that there is eventually more trust in qi-power and the ground than in will-power.

Lying

Lying down requires very little strength and energy. It is easy to relax in this position, but there is a danger of becoming drowsy or falling asleep. Undoubtedly this helps if you have insomnia, but sleepiness is generally an unwanted effect in Qi Gong.

Lying down is a position in which severely sick people, people with a very weak constitution or certain disabled people might practise Qi Gong.

Sitting

Sitting is the classical way of doing quiet and meditative Qi Gong. Whether you sit on a chair, a cushion or on the floor; whether you sit in a half-lotus, lotus, on your heels or with your legs simply crossed, depends on the exercise and on what you are used to. It is always better to choose a way of sitting in which you feel comfortable enough to stay relaxed.

If you sit on a chair, be sure that your feet rest fully on the ground. Place them parallel to each other, toes pointing to the front, shoulder-width apart. You might need to sit slightly forward on the chair in order to have your feet comfortably flat. Imagine that your feet and the earth really belong to each other; that they're really meeting.

As the centre point of gravity is quite deep when you sit, this posture is good for concentrating on the dan tian, enhancing the experience that you are firm below in the belly area, and empty above, in the upper torso and head. If not mentioned otherwise, the hands rest on the thighs, palms up; the chin is slightly tucked in.

In most sitting exercises the emphasis is on outer stillness and inner movement. By sitting still you give space for the internal movements of qi.

Standing

Standing requires more strength and energy. It might surprise you how difficult it is at first to stand for some time with relaxed knees and the weight equally balanced on both feet. Standing in a stiff and unbalanced way stops Earth qi flowing up the legs, it cuts off the contact with inner and outer nature and signals a wavering trust and loss of safety in the world. If the stance is weak and stiff, the person's energy is unbalanced, not grounded, hanging in the air. Being centred as a person presupposes a natural way of standing and being connected with Mother Earth.

The art of standing is essential in Qi Gong and has been practised for centuries by Qi Gong and martial arts practitioners. It is not only about physical strength, but also about rooting, grounding, re-aligning the body and centring the whole person. A good way to learn this art is to practise the Qi Gong stance, which is taught in many variations, all grounded in common basic principles.

You might learn the stance in three sequences.

EXERCISE 6: QI GONG STANCE 1

1   Stand with feet parallel, toes pointing to the front, about shoulder-width apart; your knees are slightly bent. The weight is distributed equally between both feet. Try to relax your legs, knees and feet while staying in this posture. Imagine that all tension is melting down deep into the earth.

2   Visualize roots growing from the soles of your feet and reaching deep down in the soil. The soil supports you with energy. You can imagine that the actual ground you are standing on is a sandy beach, rich forest soil, a meadow or some other ground you like.

3   The upper body, the spine and the head are upright without being stiff, the chin slightly tucked in. The eyes are half-closed, looking straight ahead without focusing. Relax the neck; imagine that your spine is being gently pulled at both ends. Cast your mind quietly over the main joints of the body, and consciously loosen them: shoulders, elbows, wrists, hips, knees and ankles.

4   Stand like this for maybe five minutes; stay in contact with your body, looking inside, being aware of energy movements, tensions, breathing and mental activity.

The second sequence includes the principle full below/empty above. The focus is on the abdominal area, on the dan tian. The lower part of the body is stable, vibrant, full, compared to the relatively empty, light and transparent feeling in the upper body. Qi is brought back to its origin, the abdominal area, the ideal place to store it. For here is the engine-house of your energy, the battery. The effect is of feeling well centred and having a store of energy available for when it might be needed.

EXERCISE 7: QI GONG STANCE 2

1   Resume the posture of the first sequence. Be aware of the lower part of your body. By doing so your breathing might become deeper. Be aware of how your whole abdominal area expands gently when you breathe in. Gently flatten the curve of your spine in the lower back a little bit by slightly tucking in the lower pelvis.

2   Imagine that there are five rubber bands: one around your hips, one around each knee and one around each ankle. When you breathe in they expand, with the out-breath they contract again.

3   Be aware of energy movements, breathing, body feelings. Compare the feeling in the upper part of the body with the feeling in the lower part.

Through ongoing concentration on the firmness and fullness of the lower body, the upper part eventually becomes empty and transparent. Remember the image of the branches moving freely and lightly.

EXERCISE 8: QI GONG STANCE 3

1   Repeat the posture of the first sequence, and also the emphasis on the lower part of the body as in sequence 2. Now slowly raise your arms to shoulder height, as if embracing a tree trunk. Try to keep the elbows round to form a circle with the arms. The fingers are slightly spread, about an inch apart from each other. Imagine that your body is suspended on five silken threads: one at each elbow, one at each wrist and one at the top of the head.

2   Be sure that your shoulders are not raised and/or in tension. Tell yourself that you don't need any muscular power to hold your arms because they are held by four threads. If there is tension, let it flow out of the body via the finger tips.

In the beginning it might be difficult to hold the arms like this. The opportunity is to learn to release tension without changing the posture. You are aware of the tension and eventually melt it by your imagination. If this is too hard, drop the arms a so the palms face the belly, the dan tian. You can also release the arms, shake arms and hands, and then gently resume the posture.

The paradoxical instruction, once more, is effortless effort. You are not forcing yourself, yet you are willing to persevere and to observe quietly what happens to tension or tiredness while you are in the posture. You are willing to observe if the posture changes and you lose balance or lightness, and softly then to make adjustments. When you stand, your roots dig deep into Earth, and the silken thread from the crown of your head reaches into Heaven. This is a key image in Qi Gong. Even when you change to movement, the imprint of the stance remains as a significant symbol, an archetypal reference point.

There are thousands of exercises in Qi Gong! These divide roughly into two categories:

✦ **Dong Gong**, also called active Qi Gong, exercises in movement, outer exercises, **Wai Gong**

✦ **Jing Gong**, also called passive Qi Gong, quiet Qi Gong, **Nei Gong** (inner work) or meditative Qi Gong.

Jing Gong is done mostly sitting, sometimes standing; there is hardly any outer movement. Dong Gong is done mostly standing or moving, very occasionally sitting. There is outer movement, which is balanced by inner stillness and centredness. This inner stillness is not absolute. Contained in it is the movement of qi as it anticipates imaginatively the physical movement to come.

A common feature of all exercises in **movement** is the co-ordination between movement, a quiet state of mind and breathing. The movements are mostly slow, floating, graceful and rounded. Exercises can be short and relatively easy to learn or include elaborate choreography.

Examples of classical movement forms are: The Eight Brocades, Bone Marrow Cleansing and Five Animal Frolics. Wild Goose and Flying Crane Qi Gong are more recent forms. These forms are elaborate and very difficult to learn from a book. The same is true for bagua, and tai ji quan which are sometimes considered as forms of Qi Gong, but are mostly seen as being in a category of their own.

A simple, classical exercise, easy to learn from a book, is Holding up the Sky. We follow Wong Kiew Kit's version.

EXERCISE 9: HOLDING UP THE SKY

1   Take the Qi Gong stance. Your arms hang loosely by your side. With the in-breath lift your hands gently in front of your body, up to your chest, palms upwards, fingers pointing towards each other; then turn the hands slowly so that the palms face downward and, with the out-breath, push down as if meeting resistance from the air. Push – without muscular effort – until the arms are fully stretched, without stiffening. There is tension where the wrists bend at right angles from the arm, fingers pointing towards each other.

2   With the next in-breath, keeping the hands and arms in this stretched position, follow the extension of the arms, bringing them in a half-circle before the body until they are above your head. The arms are now in an out-stretched position over the head, the wrists bent at right angles, the hands about an inch apart. Having followed the last part of this manoeuvre with your eyes, your head is now slightly tilted

back and you are gazing through the gap between your hands, Holding up the Sky. This entire upward arc should be done with the in-breath, so adapt your pace to your own breathing rhythm.

3   Once the hands are stretched above the head, hold the breath for as long as is comfortable. Keep your shoulders relaxed but feel the stretch along the outer sides of the torso.

4   With the out-breath, let the arms float slowly downwards, keeping them outstretched to the right and left of the body, palms down and wrists loosening. The head returns slowly to its normal position.

5   Let the arms come to rest once more either side of the body and then repeat from 1 with your next in-breath.

BREATHING

We are being breathed from the first to the last moment of our life: we can't start it ourselves, we can't stop it ourselves. Breathing seems to be the easiest and most natural process. But is it?

Natural breathing, an ingredient of Qi Gong practice, is not normal breathing for most of us. As breathing and emotions are highly connected to each other, our emotional history leaves its imprint on our breathing pattern, which can be disturbed and restricted. In body psychotherapy we see people with depressive tendencies who don't dare to breathe in fully, to take in the energy freely available for all of us. More rigid or uptight people, afraid of losing control, stop themselves breathing out fully in order to avoid losing control, or surrendering too much to life. There is chronic rapid breathing, which is an inability to breathe slowly and come to rest. There is flat breathing, where movements are restricted only to the chest. This is a sign of someone wanting to control 'gut feelings', going through the world with a stiff upper lip or the chest blown up in a military way in order to hide weakness and to look powerful.

If you watch a young child or an animal breathing you see a graceful and effortless co-ordination of different body movements. There is movement in the chest, the rib cage, belly and lower back. A key factor in breathing is the flexibility of the muscle of the diaphragm.

With the in-breath, the diaphragm contracts and sinks down, giving space for the lungs – especially the lower lobes – to be filled with air. With the out-breath, the diaphragm relaxes, rising again, pushing the used air up and out. If this natural capacity of the diaphragm is disturbed, or if it is in chronic tension, or frozen, breathing becomes inefficient.

Practising Qi Gong helps to re-establish more natural breathing, which is unforced and easy; quiet in an unrestricted way. Ideally, breathing in Qi Gong is slow, long, deep, fine, regular and tranquil. It is often very soft, sometimes even hardly visible. It is very different from the strong and dramatic 'taking a good breath', which is quite often an ineffective puffing out of the chest. Softness in Qi Gong breathing is due to relaxation, a quiet mind and efficient breathing; it does not arise from the imposition of restrictions as in flat breathing.

Usually Qi Gong practitioners breathe in and out through the nose, or in by the nose and out through the mouth. Breathing in through the nose has distinct physiological advantages. It filters, warms and moisturizes the air; it also helps you to reach a meditative mood. Some people prefer breathing out by mouth because it makes relaxation easier.

Changing breathing patterns is more than a technical task. As breathing is deeply interwoven with acquired personality, changes in life-style, psychological and spiritual growth, have a distinct effect on the breathing pattern; equally, improvement of breathing has a big impact on the psychological and spiritual self. So you can see that working with breathing is a difficult but also rewarding task, with unexpected effects in unexpected quarters.

This process of re-establishing a natural breathing pattern needs patience and a friendly attitude towards yourself. It can't be forced. If you have severe breathing problems, if you stay unchanged in a disturbed pattern for a long time, or if you become flooded by anxiety when breathing deeper, you should consult an expert.

There are three ways of working with breathing in Qi Gong.

✦ Don't pay any attention to breathing. By practising Qi Gong the body learns to relax, the mind becomes calmer and as a result of this the breathing becomes more natural.

✦ Stay aware of your breathing, watching it in a non-judgemental way without doing any explicit breathing exercises.

✦ Do breathing exercises.

We recommend – especially for beginners – the second possibility as a foundation for working with breathing. It is the Taoist way to watch inner nature working. While you are in a state of kind awareness and focus, you notice how the body re-organizes a healthy breathing pattern.

EXERCISE 10: WATCHING YOUR BREATH

Sit still on a chair, relax, watch your breathing. Try to be non-judgemental, there are no shoulds or should-nots. Be aware of what is. If your breathing changes, follow it with your awareness. Don't change anything wilfully, don't force anything. Let your breath lead you; don't try to lead your breath.

You can use this as a non-directive breathing exercise or as a start for your Qi Gong practice, preparing you to become still, to relax and to look inside.

Your breathing could soon become deeper and quieter. You are on your way back to natural breathing. This can be quite a journey: an adventurous journey. As soon as your body has a glimpse of natural breathing it will long for more of this experience and invite you to go on.

While in natural breathing you are simply aware of how the breath comes and goes, in **dan tian breathing** the focus is on dan tian and abdominal movements. In the standing exercise we asked you to visualize a rubber band round your hips which expands and contracts with breathing. When you practise belly breathing you are consciously aware of all of these movements and you might even use a *little bit* of muscular effort to reinforce them.

Belly breathing eventually has the effect of slowing down and relaxing the breath. Breathing becomes deeper and more efficient. The diaphragm is able to sink further, giving more space to the lungs and massaging the belly organs in a soft way. By focusing on the dan tian, qi sinks down more easily, stabilizing the lower part of the body. The mind calms; you become centred.

A good way of exercising breathing is with a partner. If you feel someone's hand on a part of your body, breathing is encouraged in a non-directive way.

EXERCISE 11: BREATHING WITH A PARTNER

1   One of the partners lies down on their back. The other touches them with one hand on the breast bone –
    the middle point between the breasts – the other on the belly. The touch is soft, no pressure! Both stay
    with the breathing movements of the one who is lying down without any necessity for changing them.

2   After a while one hand stays on the belly, the other moves to the lower back.

3   After a while, the sitting partner puts left and right hands on either side of the rib cage.

4   Do this exploring quietly and peacefully. Both of you might want to share your experiences in a
    descriptive and non-judgemental way before changing roles.

CAUTION

Proceeding to more advanced Qi Gong breathing techniques, be aware that they should only be practised after
a stable belly breathing pattern has emerged. Don't try them prematurely; it will cause more harm than good.

When you watch your breath, you might realize that there are natural short breaks at the turning points
between in-breath and out-breath, and out-breath and in-breath. Focusing on these breaks creates a distinct
state of mind – meditative, connected and peaceful.

Breathing in intervals lengthens these turning points, either between in-breath and out-breath, between out-breath and in-breath, or both. Initially short, these breaks can become longer with advanced practice. Nevertheless the holding of the breath should never be forced, you should always feel comfortable while practising. We suggest you start this technique doing only one break between breathing out and breathing in, and adding silent words which support the relaxation aspect.

12

EXERCISE 12: BREATHING IN INTERVALS

1 Sit on a chair, relax. Breathe in, think the word 'I'.

2 Breathe out, think 'am'. In the break after the out-breath, think 'quiet and relaxed'.

3 Start again with in-breath and 'I', and continue.

With longer practice you can add more of your own words in the break. Always make sure you are not forcing the interval.

Paradox breathing – the next advanced technique – is also called 'hard belly breathing' as compared to the soft 'normal' belly breathing. The breathing movements are reversed: drawing in the belly with the in-breath; relaxing and expanding it with the out-breath.

Among the benefits of paradox breathing are its ability to intensify qi flow and to increase the capacity to store qi in the dan tian. It helps to include the lower back in the breathing movements. Paradox breathing is used in specific exercises and sometimes – because of the way it creates an intense contact with abdominal muscles and diaphragm – as a short preparation for other breathing exercises.

Paradox breathing seems to resemble a disturbed breathing pattern. In both, the belly is contracted with the in-breath, and expanded with the out-breath. Cohen points out that there are distinct differences: paradox Qi Gong breathing is slow, pathological reversed breathing is rapid; paradox Qi Gong breathing is calm, pathological reversed breathing has a nervous and/or anxious quality; paradox Qi Gong breathing is in touch with the dan tian, pathological breathing is cut off from the belly.

In spite of the benefits of paradox breathing, it should be confined to certain Qi Gong exercises. It is definitely not a healthy way of breathing in your everyday life.

Embryonic breathing is also called pre-natal breathing, navel breathing or – as the breathing movements are hardly visible – 'stopping the breath'. Embryonic breathing is dan tian breathing in its finest and most advanced form. It is light and effortless; you are breathed by Mother Nature as an embryo is breathed by its physical mother through the umbilical cord.

Embryonic breathing is said to cultivate pre-natal qi. It is a way of surrender to the Tao; it is a way of coming home.

Body breathing is based on embryonic breathing. It is more qi breathing than actual breathing. The in-breath comes from the surface of the whole skin. Each pore is turned outside to suck in universal qi. The qi is drawn to the dan tian, collected and compressed. There are different possibilities for the out-breath. We feature a variation in which used and exhausted qi is sent down through the legs and feet deep into the earth.

EXERCISE 13: BODY BREATHING

13

1   Take the Qi Gong standing position. Practice paradox breathing. With the in-breath imagine that your whole skin surface is sucking in fresh cosmic qi which is then drawn to the dan tian. Stay relaxed, no effort!

2   With the out-breath visualize sending all used and exhausted qi down a middle line in your legs. Imagine that it leaves the body through the soles of the feet, and is absorbed deep into the earth.

YI – THE GUIDING MIND

Yi describes the focusing and guiding function of the mind in Qi Gong. Yi can mean thought, intention, will, consciousness, awareness and imagination. By focusing awareness with will on an area of the body, the intention is to evoke certain physiological and energetic effects.

14

EXERCISE 14: GUIDING QI

Stand with the arms extended, palms down. Relax. Don't move your arms but imagine that you are pressing a big ball under water. Imagine the resistance of the ball, and feel the sensations in your palms.

You may experience a tingle or other responsive sensation in your palms. This impact upon your body is not caused by physical action but by the creativity of your mind. Words, thoughts and images – especially if emotionally charged – have a signal effect upon energetic and physiological processes. The virtual reality of a film affects us sometimes as if the experience on the screen were ours, personally. We can come into wakefulness from a frightening dream with a racing heart.

In Western thinking, this mechanism is best known in the psychosomatic field. If someone is dominated by extreme anxiety, the energy tends to be contracted, the breathing restricted, the shoulders drawn up and tense. There are numerous examples of how negative thinking and feeling patterns can have unwanted physiological effects.

Qi Gong takes positive advantage of this body-mind interaction, using the creative power of the mind to guide qi into more positive patterns. Negative thinking and feeling patterns can create a negative self-image, harmful physiological reactions and even sickness; positive thinking and feeling patterns can establish a beneficial effect upon physiological processes, state of health and general well-being.

'Body-mind interaction' is a Western way of describing this process; in Chinese thinking there is no separation of body and mind. Jing, qi and shen are different aspects of a whole. In the Three Treasures system, there is a nourishing line from jing to qi to shen, and a commanding line from shen to qi to jing. If you work with yi, you take advantage of this commanding line, make it conscious, and work with volition to guide qi to any part of the body. You can direct qi to the dan tian, as you start or finish an exercise, to any acupuncture point, along the meridians and around qi circles as in the Microcosmic Orbit (see page 98). In healing, your mind or the mind of the healer focuses on painful or sick areas of the body.

There are many healing techniques in Qi Gong ranging from the relatively simple processes such as melting away tension by concentrating on the tense area, or letting a headache stream out of the head as if it were a black cloud, to more complex systems.

Sometimes the mind is simply focused on parts of the body; sometimes visualization – images, colours, sounds – are used. A white light can be imagined cleaning the body, an inner smile wanders through the organs, the digestive tract and the spine, or qi sinks deep down into the Earth. If you have practised some of the exercises in the book, you have already encountered the use of imagery. To experience this ingredient of Qi Gong more fully, try the next exercise, which combines breathing with imagination.

EXERCISE 15: LOTUS FLOWER

1   Sit on a chair, relax, quieten down. If you are already at ease with belly breathing and paradox breathing, change to paradox breathing; otherwise breathe normally.

2   Imagine an open lotus flower – it could also be a sunflower or any other flower that comes immediately to your imagination – at the base of your pelvic floor.

3   As you breathe in, the flower is lifted up, its petals closing, no further than the lower end of the rib cage. With the out-breath the flower sinks down again, the petals opening and spreading at the very base of your pelvic floor.

4   With the next in-breath it rises ... Continue in this way.

Focusing the mind and using visualization are delicate techniques. They need a relaxed, quiet state, receptivity. At the same time, the mind has to be active, guiding qi. Even with this intention and will, there is no forcing. As the Chinese say, it is like thinking and not thinking.

The guiding function of the mind has special benefits for beginners doing quiet Qi Gong. Sometimes it is difficult for beginners to feel qi. Telling them to collect qi in the dan tian might provoke questions like, 'How can I feel my dan tian? How do I feel the qi that is to be collected?' As a start, imagining that there is a powerful battery or a small flame between the navel and the pubic bone, you substitute imagination for the actual experience. After some practice – as qi follows yi – there will be an actual sensation. When you practise the qi circle called Microcosmic Orbit (see page 98), yi first guides qi all the way up the spine to the crown and down the middle line of the front of the body. Most beginners don't have sensations of qi all along the circle; there are missing links, which have to be 'bridged' by yi. After further practice these stuck areas might open up to allow a subjective perception of qi. For advanced practitioners yi becomes less important: qi and yi eventually fall together to become one.

ENDING

To do a Qi Gong exercise without ending is like planting without harvesting. Ending – shou gong – is a distinct process in itself. It rounds off the experience by collecting qi and enjoying the fruits of practice. It smoothes the transition to other activities.

Collect qi by focussing your awareness in the dan tian for some time. Stay in this awareness until you have a subjective feeling of qi settling deep down. This usually goes with a feeling of roundness and completion. Try these two visualizations after practising sitting Qi Gong.

16

EXERCISE 16: ENDING 1

Breathe normally. With the in-breath, imagine that a space opens up in your belly; relax with the out-breath as the qi sinks down into that space.

17

EXERCISE 17: ENDING 2

1 Change to paradox breathing.
2 With the in-breath, imagine that qi is being sucked into the dan tian. With the out-breath, relax, and let it settle.

When you have completed an exercise with movement, stay a while, eyes closed or open but unfocused, and concentrate on your dan tian. To reinforce the focus, put both hands on the dan tian, or hold the hands away from the dan tian, palms facing the body, and draw the hands back towards dan tian as if you were squeezing a balloon into your belly.

After collecting qi, the transition to daily life should be gentle and unhurried. You might have emerged from a deep and quiet space, especially if you've done inner Qi Gong, and it's a shock if you end brusquely. During the time of transition, slowly allow your six roots to become aware of outer surroundings. Rub your face or do some other self-massage. If you've been sitting, have a good stretch.

DISTURBANCES

In Qi Gong practice, energy and body undergo a process of re-organization. As the breathing becomes more natural, as the qi flow intensifies, as the mind quietens down and the posture adjusts, there are various side-effects, some of which are uncomfortable. This discomfort is sharpened by enhanced sensitivity developed through practice. You will enjoy feeling energetic and alive; you might also experience itching, sweating and unusual patches of heat, watering eyes or excessive yawning. There might be a distinctly increased or decreased appetite, an enhanced flow of saliva, loud belly noises, belching, active peristalsis and increased bowel activity.

Be aware of these minor disturbances but don't give them too much attention. With growing practice, or by talking to a teacher, you might train yourself to differentiate between positive, harmless and negative effects.

The qi flow manifests mostly in sensations of streaming, tingling or pulsing. You might also experience vibration or even shaking, when qi enters a blocked area. Think of an old car, unused for many years, and how it reacts when it is started up! This kind of breakthrough is also signalled by itching, named therefore 'the first step through the door'. The initial shaking or itching feeling disappears after some time when the qi flows freely.

Shaking can have another quality: continuous, rough, regular and heavy. You can interpret this kind of shaking in two different ways. Either you are exhausted and should think about ending a strenuous exercise or practice altogether. Or, on the other hand, your body might be in an ongoing process of de-armouring and melting away tensions. In spontaneous Qi Gong this is a welcome experience.

Finally, there is a third kind of vibrating: subtle, constant, hardly visible, fine, humming, signalling strong and healthy qi flow.

So, vibration can have different meaning and consequence, and you need to develop an inner awareness. The same is true for pain. There is pain, signalling the melting of tension, a 'melting pain' which is almost sweet, showing that the tension is finally giving way to streaming. Imagine re-entering a warm house after a long walk on a cold and snowy day. Your hands are frozen, and as they thaw indoors, the feeling of melting and streaming is painful. So it is in Qi Gong, as the currents of energy start to enter hitherto blocked and resistant areas of the body. The best way of accommodating this experience is willingly to open up to the melting and streaming, breathing down with the sensation as it happens.

Up to now we have talked about disturbances as a by-product of correct practice. There's another category of disturbance, and this is to do with incorrect practice. For example:

✦ insufficient relaxation; too much tension in the body;

✦ inadequate or forced breathing;

✦ mental or emotional restlessness; forced imagination or over-expectation of results.

The disturbances arising from incorrect practice are, for example, **headaches and dizziness**. These commonly result from emotional tension or excessive motivation. If you are over-concerned with progress or results, you might force your will-power and imagination, or push down frustration, impatience and agitation under a false sense of calmness.

Further disturbances can be located around **breathing difficulties** and feelings of **constriction in the chest**. Underlying this could be that you are forcing your breath or giving it too much anxious attention. The origin of this difficulty might also be located around emotional problems or tension in the shoulders and chest. Once more, relaxation, with a special focus on slow breathing, is the best solution. If you are still under stress, stretch your arms from side to side, and encourage yawning and sighing.

If you experience **heart palpitations**, the root cause could possibly be an unquiet spirit, a tense mood and/or a disturbed breathing pattern. Try to dive underneath the excitation, focusing on calm belly breathing and relaxation.

Over-indulgence in forced deep belly breathing or over-doing the intervals in the interval breathing sequence can create a **bloated feeling** as if you've eaten too much! In this case, return to light and natural breathing.

Just as you have to deal with physical and emotional problems, you especially need to manage the **restless mind**. The mind will always think. It is programmed for this and you can't stop it. Try to accept mental activity and the invariably constant rising and falling of feelings and body reactions without getting caught up in it. Dive under the noise, return to dan tian. Learning not to identify with this restlessness is a continuous refinement through awareness. Let the mind come and go, as if it were a radio playing softly in the next room.

Another resistance of the mind, the polar opposite of restlessness, is **indolence or drowsiness**. Notice, especially in quiet Qi Gong classes, a few people drowsing away, falling asleep and snoring! You might be delighted that Qi Gong can induce immediately refreshing sleep – but remember that this is mostly a form of resistance and an unwanted effect. When affected by drowsiness, keep your eyes half-open when doing meditative exercises.

A disturbance, nothing to do with you, could come from the outside as you practise. A loud noise, for example. In this case, imagine – several times – breathing out the effects of the intrusion or the shock.

In all this exploration of factors disturbing to your practice, your own awareness and discrimination emerge as significant. If there is any symptom that persists and is unusually uncomfortable or painful, stop practice and see a Qi Gong expert or your doctor. Learn how to judge whether your symptoms are momentary or severe, and act accordingly. It is also worth reminding you that if you are particularly tense or restless, sometimes the shaking exercise (Return of Spring) from the warm-up section is a useful preliminary to more quiet forms of relaxation.

THE TAO OF PRACTICE

Qi Gong, even if practised without reference to any philosophical or spiritual system, is permeated with the principles of Taoism. Taoist notions create a field in which to practise – a field of paradox which requires you to balance apparent opposites.

Let's start with **wu-wei** – non-doing. Misunderstood as a manifestation of Eastern fatalism, it describes in reality a delicate inner process. Wu-wei is not forcing, non-interference, a policy of naturalness, non-assertion, acting without intention, giving way, actionless action, effortlessness.

An image of wu-wei arises when you observe skilled and devoted craftsmen. They embody their work and are at one with their material and tools. Movements are simple and economical, full of grace; nothing is fumbling, flamboyant or forced. Think of an Indian tea-maker. In a tiny space, he performs his art with light, easy movements. The tea flies in a liquid arc from cup to cup. Watching him, it feels as if he has been doing this for centuries; watching him, it feels as if he's not doing it at all, the action is moving through him, and he allows it to happen, without thought. Witness a tai ji practitioner in a forest clearing or next to a lake. The movements, like those of the tea-maker, seem to come from another source, from a fresh and archetypal place where there is neither hesitation nor artifice. Think of yourself struggling with a thorny problem. No resolution comes from effort or forced thinking. You give up, and, in the release of tension, an open and receptive state is restored – an image or thought of a different quality arrives . Aha! That's it! This quality is of whole intelligence, rather than pressurised mental intelligence. If you are still and receptive, that intelligence can move over fertile ground ... if you are anxious or too wilful, you have created obstacles in the way of this free-flow.

Taoists are fond of water and use it as a metaphor for action and attitude in accordance with the Tao. Water seems weak: it is yielding; occupies the lowest position. Yet, it is the most powerful of the elements, finding its way through rocks, extinguishing fire. To follow the Watercourse Way is to avoid spending any more energy than needed. Working with, rather than against, nature. Crossing a river? Use the flow of the water. Don't go against the current, don't be washed away by it. Windsurfing? Stand on a board and use the elemental forces of water and wind. Sounds easy, but it is not. To windsurf effortlessly, you need practice, experience and knowledge, a flexible stance, a relaxed and alert body, strength, patience and understanding of how to direct your sail, and deal with different waves and winds. You'd have to learn just as you learn standing, breathing and moving in Qi Gong. And one day, after you'd been thrown into the water many times, your body and mind would find the effortless way. You are one with the wind and the waves. Wu-wei! So wu-wei doesn't mean lazily waiting for a divine spark to transmit Qi Gong knowledge. As in windsurfing, you need discipline, perseverance, and surrender to that which is beyond your conscious control, a surrender that allows inner nature to do its work.

What does this mean? Turn your attention inwards now, as you read the next section. Let an image or a perception arise, showing how you experience apparently opposing forces: active as in discipline, will, action; passive as in surrender, stillness, letting-go.

You might recognize your predominantly self in one of the following figures:
(the white zones represent the active polarity; the black zones represent the passive polarity)

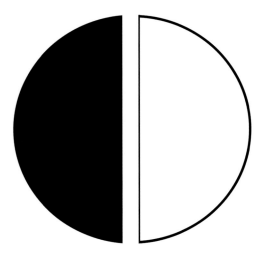

Figure 1 Your black and white are strictly separated, there's a gap between them, with no possible smooth transition from one to the other. You work ceaselessly and then collapse through exhaustion onto the other side; you lift yourself from collapse by strength of will or artificial stimuli, back over the great divide into the active section.

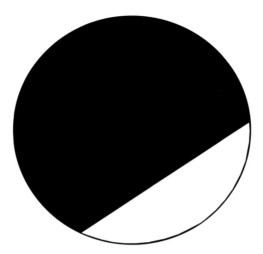

Figure 2 Your main identification is with the passive section, and because there is no regulation from the active, the dark quality is less to do with relief and surrender, and more to do with inertia and stagnation.

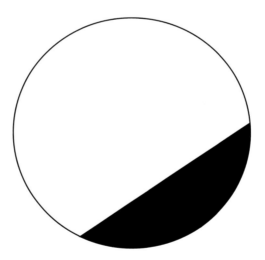

Figure 3 Your main identification is with the active field. Here, the regulating force of the passive field is missing. Your active state has a manic quality to it, less to do with grounded action and more to do with being driven and out-of-control.

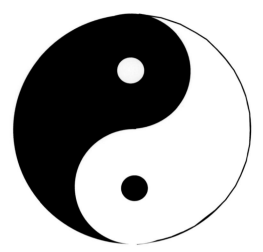

You might find yourself in **Figure 4**. You are in the Tao! Both forces are equally present, and yet each has a drop of the other implicit in it. Together they make a harmonious whole. If you've found yourself in Figure 4, enjoy being in the Tao and abandon the rest of the chapter. If you're like most of us, read on...

Balancing polarities is at the core of Taoism, and at the core of Qi Gong. Qi Gong exercises are choreographed according to the laws of polarity: sinking and rising, contracting and expanding, opening and closing. According to the Taoists, you are a mediator between Earth and Heaven, harmonising Yin and Yang, feminine and masculine, receptivity and penetration, the energies of your body with the subtle energies of your spirit, reconciling opposites and transforming them, coming back home to the One.

Let's come back to practice. Let's look at another polarity: doing as your teacher tells you, or trusting your own feelings. Living only one side of the polarity would be to imitate the instructions blindly; living the other would be to ignore the instructions and do your own thing. The seduction is to go into the either/or trap.

The Taoist way is to blend the two into one. You've been shown a movement, where the arms are outstretched above the head. You follow the instruction, but at the same time, you look inside to check your reality. You realize that your shoulders are tense. You relax your shoulders and this brings you to a more natural flow. Again referring to the instruction you are told that stretching your arms is connected to the out-breath. You take this information in, respond correctly, but at the same time, co-ordinate your breathing with your movement. In this way you are working with your own direct experience and with the teaching; fine-tuning and adjusting.

If you have a good teacher, you are fortunate to receive formal instruction and enter the spirit of the exercise too. But even then you know your exercise is the same and not the same. There is no absolutely correct way to do an exercise. Instructions are guide-lines, maps. The authentic landscape is within you.

In your motivation to do Qi Gong, you inevitably develop expectations and ideals. The irony is the more you want, the less you get. It's like chasing an orgasm! Of course everyone has expectations. The art is not to identify with them or take them too seriously.

Moving with Qi – Active Qi Gong

Five easy-to-learn exercises from the many on offer give you a taste of the moving art of Qi Gong.

18

EXERCISE 18: CIRCLING THE BALL

Take the Qi Gong stance, knees slightly bent, arms hanging loosely by your side.

1   With the in-breath, allow the arms to float up, outstretched in front of you, palms down, until they are parallel to the ground, at shoulder height. The hands hang lightly from the wrists.

2   Continuing the in-breath, allow the arms to be drawn back towards your body, as if they were sliding over the surface of a ball. While you do this, the hands change position slowly and smoothly from palms downward to fingers up and palms outward.

3   When the arms have been drawn back as far as they will go and the hands are just in front of the chest in this upward and outward position, start to breathe gently out and press the hands downwards. When your hands reach hip level, let them hang loose for a moment and release any tension in your body. Allow the hands to rise again, with the in-breath, repeating the exercise as often as you wish. Keep gently adjusting the co-ordination so that you come more and more in line with your own natural rhythms.

4   After you have become accustomed to the movement, imagine that you follow the surface of a ball that is hanging in front of your body, or, more subtly, allow that surface to draw your hands effortlessly along, towards you, downwards and upwards. The breathing and the movement of arms and hands synchronize to create a feeling of roundness, effortless rising and falling. Your arms hang softly as if held from the wrists by threads, and eventually, the co-ordination is such that it's not easy to distinguish whether the movement seems to come out of the breathing, or the breathing out of the movement. Hold the idea that breathing in creates expansion, lightness and up-ness; breathing out creates release, gravity and down-ness. Imagine waves rising before they break and roll along the beach. If you're lucky enough to be on a beach, do this exercise along the water's edge!

This exercise helps you to relate your breathing rhythm to movements, and to feel the ongoing circularity of natural breathing.

19

EXERCISE 19: PUNCHING

Take the Qi Gong stance, but wider and deeper than usual. Sink your feet into the ground, tuck in your tailbone and make sure your head rests straight and easy on your shoulders, chin slightly tucked in. Feel the energy in your dan tian and release any tension in the belly.

1 Both hands form soft fists, not clenched but loosely held; elbows bend so that the wrists rest lightly just at the side of your waist, the inner sides of the fists upwards.

2 Gaze – concentrated but not with force – straight ahead.

3 Punch forward with the right hand, swivelling the forearm. There is still a slight bend in the elbow by the time the punch ends. The inner side of the fist faces downwards.

4 As you pull back the right hand, slowly rotate the fist again so that it arrives at the hip with palm upwards. At the same time, as the right hand pulls back, the left fist starts to move forward.

5 Keep rotating in this way. The movements should be fluid and certain, rather than jerky or aggressive. Make sure that your back remains in a soft, upright position, that you don't lean forward to follow the punch.

This exercise from the 'Eight Brocades' was originally called 'Punching with angry gaze to increase qi and strength'. It combines different manifestations of the Wood Element. On an emotional level the Wood Element connects to self-assertion – and can manifest as anger. The connected organ is the liver, the connected orifice the eyes. If you look angry, the liver 'opens into the eyes', meaning that you clear your liver of toxic energy and re-balance your meridians. This demonstrates the unity of emotional and bodily processes, explored later in the BodyTao chapter. You don't have to be angry to do this exercise! Think about reinforcing your self-assertion, your ground in the world, and express this through your gaze. The emphasis is on self-assertion, not on hitting or punching an 'enemy' out there.

Beginners, particularly, punch in an unbalanced way. Wanting to look fierce they engage in wild punching directed outwards, leaning forwards and losing balance. If there was an enemy he would take their hand and use their imbalance to draw them down with their own energy! So be aware of your stance, stay rooted, feel your energy in the dan tian and how this inner energy prepares for and accompanies the outwards punching movement of the arms.

Exercise 20: CARRYING THE MOON

Take the Qi Gong stance.

1   With the out-breath, bend down in a slow, conscious and organic way. Feel the weight of your head, give in to it, and allow it to roll loosely and easily downwards, vertebra by vertebra. Continue rolling the vertebrae of your upper back until you are bending over, arms and head hanging loosely. Go down as far as you are comfortable. You don't have to touch the ground, so nothing needs to be forced. (You might also notice that the more you do this exercise, the more flexibility you acquire.)

2   When you have bent down – at the end of the out-breath – stay a while and imagine a stream of qi from the base of your spine to the crown of your head.

3   With the next in-breath, effortlessly raise yourself to full height. Imagine your hips and hip joints

working as a fulcrum to raise you. Your arms are outstretched, palms down, and move to a position directly and fully-stretched above your head.

4   Letting your head fall comfortably backwards, make an arc of your body, and, with the backs of your hands facing towards you, spread your fingers at an angle to each other, so that the two index fingers form the two sides of a triangle, and the thumbs, pointing straight at each other, form the base. Keep the hands slightly apart from each other.

5   Look through the triangle as if carrying the moon, holding your breath.

6   Then exhale gently, coming back to an upright position and releasing the arms, allowing them to sink down the left and right sides, still in the outstretched position, pushing with palms downwards until your arms are again by your side.

If you've done this moving sequence – you can do it as often as you like – you might receive an immediate impact from its cleansing and energizing effects. Wong Kiew Kit, whose version of the exercise we have adapted, talks of a waterfall of vital energy when lowering the arms and breathing out, which washes away toxic energy and negative emotions deep into the soil and refreshes the whole body-mind system. He thinks that practising this exercise cultivates youthfulness. At the end – as with any other exercise – stay quiet for some time, harvesting the fruits of your work.

EXERCISE 21: REACHING AND GROUNDING

Take the Qi Gong stance.

1   Bend down as in the exercise Carrying the Moon.

2   As in the Carrying the Moon exercise, allow the arms to rise until both arms are extended vertically, either side of your head.

3   Keep the shoulders soft and relaxed. Allow the head to drop back slightly.

4   While concentrating on your feet, rooting them deeply into the ground, slightly flex your fingertips and feel how these movements invigorate qi-flow.

5   Imagine, at the same time, through the stretch, that there is emptiness and spaciousness between your organs, between the cells of your body. Stand for a moment and savour the experience of rootedness in the feet, emptiness and spaciousness in the body, and energy in the fingertips.

6   With the fingertips continuing to fill with qi, lower the hands so that the palms face towards the back of your head. Draw the hands slowly down behind the back of your head, move your hands round to the front, over the throat, and then draw them down over the torso and belly, then left and right over the backside, down the backs of the legs as you bend your knees. In all these hand-movements, you are not actually touching your body: your hands are about one inch away. Sense how your palms send qi.

7   Scoop up between the feet, and bring the hands along the inside of the legs, moving upwards along the torso until you reach chest height.

8   Spread your arms either side of you, palms outwards, and then let them float gently once more to the vertical position above your head. Hold this position once more, stretching, breathing and emptying until you feel ready to begin movement again. Your breathing should be natural and light throughout the exercise.

9   When you have completed – and the number of repetitions is up to you – bring the hands up from the ground to chest height.

10 Then turn the hands over and press downwards, as if squeezing a ball of energy into the dan tian. Place the hands over the dan tian and close your eyes, collecting qi into the dan tian.

This exercise is taken from Zhixing Wang's Hua Gong teaching. Imagination reinforces its effects. Your imaginative focus reaches into Heaven and brings down qi through your fingertips. The qi is so fine that it has the quality of silk. The silk, as it were, brushes away the dusty, static, tired qi, combing it deep down into the Earth.

In this poignant exercise, the spine is subtly and simultaneously stretched from both ends. Stretched between Heaven and Earth, space is made between organs and – imaginatively – between cells. This gives a subtle, light and spacious feeling as qi – unobstructed – permeates the whole body. Let the breathing happen naturally, though you may notice a tendency to breathe in while moving upwards and out while combing downwards.

EXERCISE 22: FLYING WILD GOOSE

93

Stand, relaxed in the Qi Gong position.

1   Your feet are grounded and stable. You are also aware of the chest, shoulder and arm area. Keep your chin softly tucked in, head straight and light, as if held on a thread.
2   With the in-breath, allow your arms to float upwards, either side of you.
3   When the arms are stretched out left and right, shoulder height, breathe out and allow them slowly to fall, pushing gently downwards with the palms of the hands. Slightly bend the knees.
4   Repeat the upward movement with the next in-breath.

The image in this exercise is of a wild goose in flight, its body stream-lined, its wings beating slowly and surely through the air. Allow the energy and impact of this image to filter through your body. When you move your arms, imagine that your breath itself, or the buoyancy of the air around you, causes them to rise and fall, gracefully and yet with power.

The exercise – meditative and cooling – helps relaxation and balance, loosens and opens joints, and strengthens legs and inner organs. It is effective in dealing with fatigue, and useful during convalescence. The exercise is an adaptation from Michael Tse.

A BRIEF WORD ABOUT THE CLASSICS...

The classical forms of Qi Gong have passed through different eras, schools and teachers. Each influence through time has left an imprint, but behind the variations, the fundamentals remain. The most popular of these forms are the Eight Brocades, Five Animal Frolics and tai ji quan. The Flying Crane and Wild Goose are considered to be classics, although their origin is recent.

The **Eight Brocades** were designed to strengthen the body and also to lengthen the muscles through gentle stretching. The exercises are connected with specific parts of the body and organs, and a sample of the names gives a ready sense of the intention: 'seven-fold spinal stretch to expel the myriad ailment', 'embracing the legs with two arms to make the kidneys firm and strong', and 'turning the head and twisting the tail to expel fire from the heart'.

The **Five Animal Frolics** is a powerful form to enhance health and strength. Hua Tuo – creator of the original form – chose crane, bear, monkey, tiger and deer. The characteristic qi patterns, economy of movement and fighting habits in each of these animals are the prima materia of the form. For example, the bear is heavy, strong, has shuffling weighty movements; the crane circles lightly in the air. The Five Animal Frolics are practised as both medical and martial Qi Gong.

Tai ji quan, the beautiful, subtly powerful and elegant form is so well known that people often ask whether Qi Gong is part of tai ji. It's more likely that tai ji is a descendant of Qi Gong, since the origins of Qi Gong date back much further. Suffice it to say that tai ji is a complete and complex set of moving postures, encapsulating the timeless play of Yin and Yang, stillness with movement, movement within stillness. tai ji can be practised as a martial art, as a moving meditation and as a vehicle for health and emotional well-being. There are many forms, varying in style and number of postures; even the relatively simple Beijing form can take many months to learn.

Flying Crane was derived in the early 1980s and is popular in both China and Europe. The form consists of five active parts in which crane movements are imitated, and a sixth part which is a standing exercise inviting spontaneous movements.

氣

Being moved by Qi – Quiet Qi Gong

MICROCOSMIC ORBIT

The Microcosmic Orbit, also called Small Qi Circle or Lesser Heavenly Cycle, is the classical exercise of Quiet Qi Gong. As the origin dates back more than 2,000 years it is not surprising that there are many variations.

Basically in this exercise qi is guided along du mai and ren mai. The word 'mai' means 'channel' and indicates a powerful human energy vessel. Du mai and ren mai are two of the Eight Extraordinary Meridians, which are not associated with a particular organ. As they are connected with many other energy pathways, they serve as potent qi reservoirs. You find important acupuncture points on both meridians.

Du mai or the Governor channel is the essential Yang-meridian, the 'sea of Yang', situated along the spine. Ren mai is the essential Yin-meridian, the 'sea of Yin', situated along a middle line in the front. Both meridians together form a circle, in which qi flows up the spine and down the front.

The Microcosmic Orbit is usually done sitting on a chair. As the guiding and experiencing of qi depends on a relaxed body, a quiet mind and natural breathing, it is wise to begin with longer preparation – for example relaxing along the four lines, watching your breath, cultivating stillness in your mind. As an additional preparation – or the only one if you are more advanced – there are three special exercises taught by Master Li Zhi-Chang.

EXERCISE 23: PREPARATION FOR QUIET QI GONG

1   Relax between your eyebrows, undoing all effort and over-determination, allowing a spacious and receptive mood. (Relaxing between the eyebrows is the opposite of frowning.)

2   Listen to sounds that are very far away ('at the edge of cosmos'), also allowing a spacious feeling and a more receptive mind.

3   Smile and allow the smiling energy to spread all over your body (and around it).

EXERCISE 24: MICROCOSMIC ORBIT

Having finished your preparations, concentrate on the dan tian. Feel the qi: it might be pulsing, streaming, warm, dense. Or something else. Or nothing at all. In this case just imagine that you feel something or visualize your qi-store below the navel. In the circle qi is guided along certain points – unlike in acupuncture you don't have to 'hit' them exactly. Deal with them instead as 'areas'.

1   Start in the **lower dan tian**, situated – as you may know by now – between the navel and pubic bone. This is your basic energy-reservoir, providing the whole body with qi. There are different opinions as to the exact location: about three thumbs below the navel; or four fifths of the way down from the navel to the pubic bone. Trust your perception. After some practice you'll have a definite feeling where your dan tian is – in terms of distance to navel and of depth inside your abdomen.

2   From the lower dan tian qi is guided down to the perineum (huiyin), situated at the base of your torso, between genitals and anus. This is an important Yin-gate connecting you with Earth qi. Relax huiyin, your genital and anal muscles, and the insides of your thighs.

3   Next you go to the tip of your **coccyx** (weilü), situated at the base of the spine.

4   Proceed to the **Gate of Life** or ming men, between the second and third lumbar vertebrae, opposite the navel. This is an essential point for cultivating pre-natal qi – you might remember that pre-natal qi is stored in the kidney area.

5 The **Great Hammer** (dazhui), between the seventh neck vertebrae – the prominent one – and the first thoracic vertebra, is positioned in a cross-road area. The vertical and horizontal axes (spine and arms) meet here.

6 Through your neck you go up to the **jade cushion**: the area at the base of the skull.

7 The **Crown** (baihui) is also called 'Heaven's door', because it is a major entry point for Heaven qi. Baihui is at the crossing point of the middle line over the head and the line connecting both ears.

8 Moving down over the forehead you reach the **Upper dan tian**. This site of the third eye, Heaven's Eye, is connected with subtle perceptions and is said to be the seat of shen. It is situated at the root of the nose between the eyebrows.

9 On your way down you pass the mouth. As ren mai and du mai are connected here you might bring your tongue to your upper palate to build a bridge. Move deeper down to the **Middle dan tian** at the breast-bone, and back to

10 **Lower dan tian.**

Repeat the circle as often as you feel comfortable and are able to stay concentrated. Always end by coming back to dan tian.

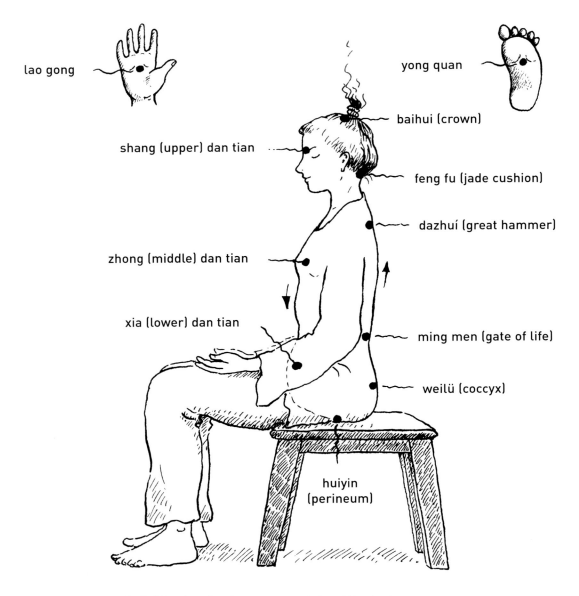

lao gong

yong quan

baihui (crown)

shang (upper) dan tian

feng fu (jade cushion)

dazhui (great hammer)

zhong (middle) dan tian

xia (lower) dan tian

ming men (gate of life)

weilü (coccyx)

huiyin
(perineum)

The Microcosmic Orbit, showing important points of the body

As you might have been in a deepened state of mind, it is wise to come back to the body by doing some self-massage after the circle. Rub your hands, stroke your face, comb your hair with your fingers, pat your head, massage your ears, massage your neck and between the shoulder blades. A last ending exercise suggested along with the others by Master Li, is circling the chin.

EXERCISE 25: THE CRANE TAKES WATER

Bend your head forward so that your chin touches the upper chest. Then move the chin up, and feel the stretch in your neck vertebrae, forward and down again so that you make a circle. Do this several times. While doing it you might visualize the Microcosmic Orbit – your chin is doing a circle that can be paralleled with the Microcosmic circle.

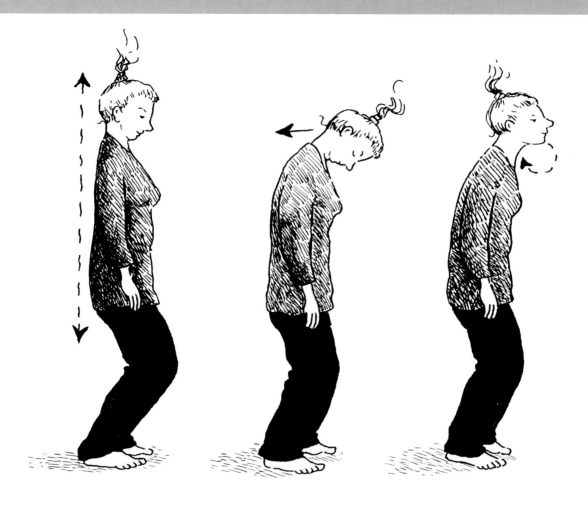

It is worth exploring the different areas you are concentrating on while doing the circle. Explore by being aware of the area, feeling its pulse, feeling energy blockages and energy flow. If there is pain, tension or numbness in one or more areas, breathe into the sensation and relax, put your hand on this area or – if you are practising with a partner or in a group – ask someone else to do this for you.

Usually, in the beginning there will be problems with distraction and drowsiness. It is not easy to stay concentrated on the circle for a long time. When you lose focus, start again with dan tian. Try to avoid 'empty' circles! It might be wise to start with relatively short exercise times – maybe 5–10 minutes – and gradually extend practice up to one hour or even more.

The main benefits of the Microcosmic Orbit are:

✦ bringing fresh qi to the main energy centres;

✦ activating the natural flow of qi. If you do the circle, qi flows much faster than under natural conditions;

✦ cleaning and loosening of tightened and blocked areas;

✦ balancing qi, distributing it according to the body's needs: taking it away from overloaded places, bringing it to needy places;

✦ harmonizing Yin and Yang.

INNER SMILE

The effect of a smile – your own or someone else's – on your well-being is obvious. In Qi Gong, smiling is used as an easy but very effective tool for relaxation, undoing stress and tensions and calming the mind and the emotions. In times of emotional turmoil or depression it might even help you to regain your self-esteem, your self-acceptance. At all times, smiling vitalizes, refreshes and rejuvenates your body-mind.

Everyone knows how to smile. Is it true that you can only smile if you feel like smiling? Smiling even if you don't feel like it brings on the inner feeling of smiling ...

26

EXERCISE 26: SMILING 1

Imagine a situation that makes you smile or visualize a wonderful natural place – it can be a real place or an imagined one – and meet a person there whom you like very much. Experience the effect of this person's smile on you and experience your own smile. Use your third eye to 'see' all the energies of the place and the person and take them in.

Be sure that you don't only smile in imagination. Experience the smiling literally by feeling the relaxing effects of the eye-wrinkles going down and the corners of the mouth going up. Allow the smile to spread like waves all over your body and around it. Let it melt your tensions, calm your mind, let it bring you a soft, light, friendly and warm feeling.

This basic exercise can be practised everywhere and always. Perhaps you don't need imagination and can simply start smiling right away. It is rewarding to practise smiling with each Qi Gong practice as a preparation, as a kind of inner warm-up.

EXERCISE 26: SMILING 1

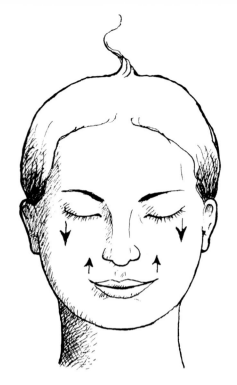

EXERCISE 27: SMILING 2

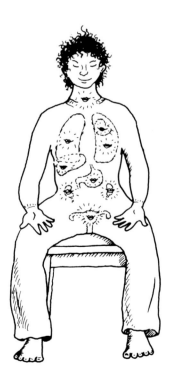
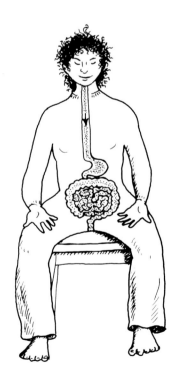
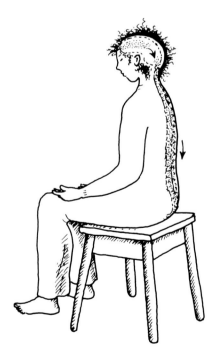

A more elaborate version of Inner Smile is taught by Master Mantak Chia.

EXERCISE 27: SMILING 2

27

After you have done smiling 1 as a preparation, actively guide the smiling energy to various parts and organs of your body. While you are concentrated on a certain part or organ, send the smiling energy there, thanking and appreciating this part of you for what it does for your life and well-being. After some time this part of the body will smile back at 'you'.

Do this along three lines:

1   Face, mouth, throat, neck, heart, lungs, liver, pancreas, spleen, kidneys, sexual organs. After this first part repeat smiling 1 to re-charge the energy.

2   Let the energy flow down to your mouth, mix it with saliva, swallow it and imagine how it sinks slowly through your whole digestive tract: oesophagus, stomach, intestines. Finally go back to re-charge energy.

3   Let the energy flow through your left and right brain, down to the jade cushion and then all the way down the spine – vertebra by vertebra.

To complete the exercise, go back once again to smiling 1: recharge the energy of your smile and let it spread without your direction wherever it wants to go, wherever it is needed. Finally collect qi in dan tian.

Smiling 2 is usually done sitting, but it also can be done standing or lying down. If it's comfortable for you, close your eyes while practising.

BUDDHA BREATHING

This exercise from the Buddhist tradition in Qi Gong looks at first just like a version of the alternate nostril breathing yoga technique. Actually the emphasis is more on qi breathing – which means guiding qi by yi – than on actual breathing. The breathing in and out of qi can be independent of actual breathing in and breathing out. Nonetheless as a beginner it is best to co-ordinate both, letting the energy of your actual breathing support the qi breathing.

The first step is to visualize the three channels in which qi is moved.

✦ The middle channel, one of the Eight Extraordinary Meridians, connecting dan tian and crown.

✦ A side channel, left of the middle channel, connecting the left nostril with dan tian.

✦ A side channel, right of the middle channel, connecting the right nostril with dan tian.

There might be individual differences in the diameter of these channels. As a rough guide Master Li, from whom we have taken this exercise, sees the middle channel as wide as a reed, the side channels more like a wheat-stalk in diameter.

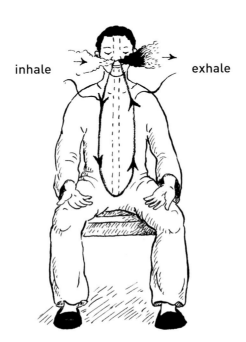

inhale   exhale

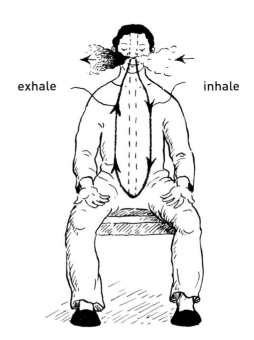

exhale   inhale

EXERCISE 28: BREATHING IN NINE SEGMENTS ACCORDING TO THE BUDDHA

Sit on a chair, relax, let your breath calm down. Visualize the three channels.

1   Breath in through your right nostril. If there are problems, use your left index finger to close your left nostril. The qi you breathe in is white and it turns red as it moves down the right side channel to the dan tian. In the dan tian qi (still red) changes over to the channel on the left, rising up, and being breathed out, as a black colour, through the left nostril.

2   Do the same on the other side: breathe in through the left nostril (white), down the left side channel (red), up the right side channel (red), breathe out through the right nostril (black).

3   Breathe in through both nostrils (white), down both side channels to dan tian (red). While you are actually breathing out, qi rises through the middle channel until just under the crown (red). While you take your next breath, qi moves down the middle channel to the dan tian (red); with the next out breath qi moves up both side channels (red) and is breathed out through both nostrils (black).

To complete the nine segments go on in the following way:

4   Start with left side, as in 2.

5   Start with right side, as in 1.

6   Start with both nostrils, as in 3.

7   Start with both nostrils, as in 3.

8   Start with right side, as in 1.

9   Start with left side, as in 2.

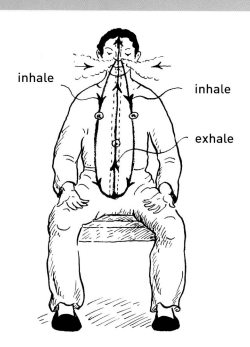

inhale

inhale

exhale

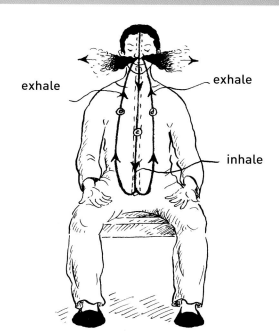

exhale

exhale

inhale

When you do this exercise, you will experience a positive impact on belly breathing: the breath will be soft, subtle and deep. Energetically it opens up the middle channel and the two side channels and balances the left and right sides of the body.

The main purpose here is cleaning. Cleaning is one of the basic activities in Qi Gong: getting rid of stale, old or even toxic qi. Cleaning can be done by various procedures such as shaking or brushing off old qi – as you do in the warm-up, breathing and visualization. The Buddha-exercise uses a combination of breathing and visualization: the more advanced you become, the less important is the breathing, and the more the emphasis is on cleaning through your spirit.

THE THREE BELLY CIRCLES

This exercise consists of three spiralling circles in the belly area. It is an excellent exercise for grounding yourself in your centre, getting in touch with spiralling movements of qi, activating and cultivating qi and increasing its volume.

EXERCISE 29: BELLY CIRCLES

Sit on a chair. After relaxing and preparing for the exercise imagine a middle point in your belly area which is between the diaphragm and perineum; front and back; left and right. Stay quietly in touch with this area. When you begin the visualization, women should start to circle clockwise while men start anti-clockwise. Women go from 1a – 1b. Men go from 1b – 1a.

1a Start the first circle from the middle point, spiralling left, down, right, up, left and so on. Let the circle get slowly bigger. Don't rush! Always stay in touch with the circling. Don't go higher than your diaphragm, or deeper than your perineum. When you reach the biggest circle, return by making the so-called tai ji slope (the s-shape which separates the two 'fish' of the Yin-Yang sign). This device enables you to change over in a soft way to the anti-clockwise movement, which brings you back to the start. Let the circles slowly reduce in size until you return to the middle point.

1b Start anti-clockwise, spiralling right, down, left, up etc ... return clockwise.

2a (Women and men both do the same.) Start the second circle again from the middle point, spiralling down, back, up, front, down and so on. The circles again increase in size, but no higher than the

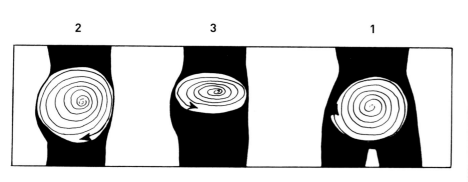

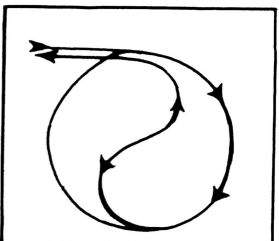

diaphragm, no deeper than perineum. After the biggest circle start to return by a tai ji slope; let the circles become smaller, return to the middle point.

2b Do it in the opposite direction by starting from the middle point, spiralling up, back, down, front, up and so on.

3 (Women start with 3a, men with 3b.)

3a Move the middle point higher, to the middle between navel and ming men (see page 100). Start to move from this higher middle point to the left, front, right, back and so on. Let the circles grow bigger until the biggest circle is like a belt around your waist. Return in a Tai ji slope for the opposite direction and then come back with smaller and smaller circles to the (higher) middle point.

3b Start the circles to the right, front, left, back, right and so on.

After doing all the circles, put both hands on dan tian. Stay for some time, collect and store qi and end the exercise.

109

You will probably have a three-dimensional feeling in your belly after practice, experiencing space, warmth and fullness in that area. Maybe you can even feel all three circles at the same time. Spirals are the most potent movement patterns in nature. Whenever you need to contact and re-establish your centre, this exercise is an excellent choice.

MERIDIAN CIRCLE

One of Qi Gong's effects is to provide an unobstructed flow of qi through the body. The pathways through which qi flows are called meridians or jing luo in Chinese. The Chinese word can be translated as 'moving through a network' which characterizes well the nature of this system. It is indeed an elaborate network of big rivers, smaller tributaries and tiny streams which are all interconnected. Each part of the body can be reached and provided with energetic nourishment.

Meridians are invisible, but we can feel the contours and currents of these energy pathways without their being materially present. Despite its elusive quality, the meridian system is an energetic reality. You find most acupuncture points on meridians and if you contact these through needle or finger pressure you will experience effects. In this way it is possible to regulate qi.

The 35 meridians of the human body can be differentiated thus:

✦ Twelve major meridians. In Western use these are named after the organ system with which they are connected, for example lung meridian, heart meridian.

✦ Eight Extraordinary Meridians, also called the Eight Miraculous Meridians. Two of them – du mai and ren mai – form the Microcosmic Orbit. The Middle Channel is used in Buddha Breathing.

✦ Fifteen collateral channels with a predominantly connecting function.

Each of the 12 'organ meridians' ends in another: together they form an ongoing circle looping three times up and down the body. A Qi Gong exercise – The Meridian Circle – follows all these 12 meridians. As this exercise is not easy to learn and requires a relatively exact knowledge of the meridian system, we present a simplified version, which bundles together several meridians in one up and one down movement.

30

EXERCISE 30: SIMPLE MERIDIAN CIRCLE

Sit on a chair, hands resting on your thighs. Feet are parallel, well connected with the ground. Relax and prepare for the exercise.

1   Concentrate on your feet, specially the yong quan points (see page 100). Imagine qi flowing from these along the inside of the legs to the perineum, and further up over both sides of the front of the body to the chest and armpits.

2   From here qi flows down the inside of the arms to the fingertips, returning over the outer hands and shoulders to the Great Hammer Point, (situated between the seventh neck vertebra and the first thoracic vertebra – the prominent one). Qi moves on over the neck and then streams upwards in all directions to the crown.

3   From there qi flows down along the sides and the back of the body and the legs to the feet.

4   Start again with the yong quan points.

5   If you want to co-ordinate qi movement with breathing, breathe in with qi rising out as it falls. Repeat as often as you like. End in dan tian, collecting qi.

EXERCISE 30: SIMPLE MERIDIAN CIRCLE

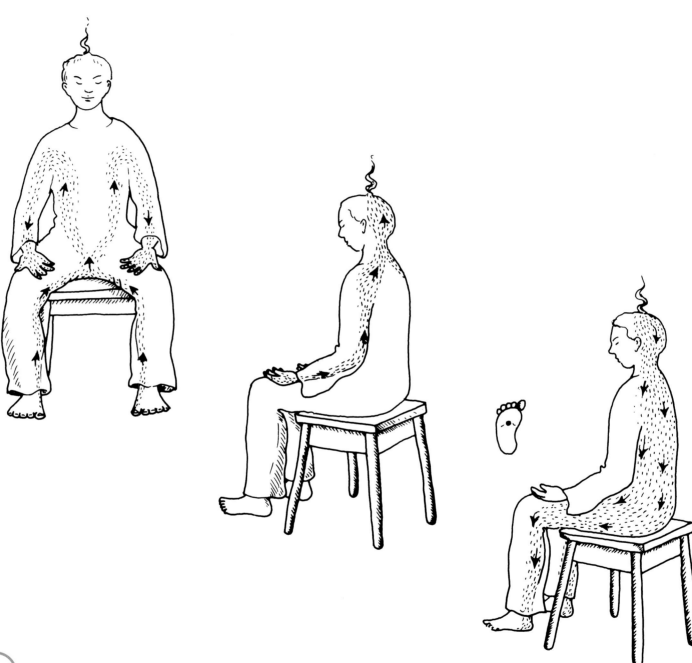

Doing this exercise you contact all 12 organ meridians:

✦ up the inside of the legs: kidney, liver and spleen meridians; all of these are Yin;

✦ down the inside of the arms: lung, pericardium and heart meridians; all of these are Yin;

✦ up the outsides of the arms: small intestine, big intestine and triple warmer meridians; all of these are Yang;

✦ down the legs: stomach, bladder and gall bladder meridians; all of these are Yang.

You don't need detailed knowledge about meridians for this exercise. You could even do it without thinking about meridians at all. However, you might want to study the course of the different meridians more closely if you want to engage more deeply in Qi Gong practice.

Letting Qi do its Work – Spontaneous Qi Gong

We invite you to enter a room full of people. Some are standing still, some moving. The movements vary from soft and rhythmic to vigorous and frenzied. You can see someone lying on the floor, another curled up in a ball near the corner. Someone else is shaking and another is bending over slowly, massaging her back. You see dancing bodies, and bodies involved in quiet absorption with one small movement, such as an arm rising and falling. Some people are singing, or continuously sounding one long note. If you've managed not to make for the nearest exit and disappear, you might wonder if you've entered Bedlam, or an encounter group regressing its members back to early childhood. Stay a while. This is what you might experience in a spontaneous Qi Gong class. 'Anarchy?' you might ask 'What's that got to do with Qi Gong?'

Spontaneous Qi Gong erupted in China in the 1980s after the time of constraint and terror connected with the Cultural Revolution, after the time of being controlled and having to keep emotions and opinions repressed. In one story the origin is connected to a particular event. A student, instructed to stand still, suddenly, unexpectedly, began moving and shaking in a strange way. Others soon followed and it spread like fire after a dry time. But surely Qi Gong always included spontaneous expression and free energetic movement which eventually condensed into form. Wong Kiew Kit, for example, suggests that as Qi Gong masters of old observed their practitioners moving freely in a variety of spontaneous movements, they labelled the movements as 'bear', 'monkey', 'deer' and so on.

Returning to our spontaneous Qi Gong class: a closer look shows us that not all is chaos or anarchy. Nor are we witnessing hypnosis, exorcism or trance. What is happening is that our inner nature is emerging in its many forms, releasing the over-loaded energy of blocked emotions, being moved by an unknown source, even enacting archetypal patterns from the collective unconscious.

This emergence is a spontaneous happening; nonetheless we need to invite spontaneity to visit us. When qi has been activated through practice, and we have afterwards cultivated a relaxed and still state, the Qi Gong state, it is possible to experience the subtle, inner movements of qi.

There's no engagement with thinking about how or where qi should move – it simply moves, and we notice it. It's like sitting in quiet company when your stomach suddenly growls. You didn't ask it to; you don't especially want it to, but it does. An arm or leg occasionally twitches, you involuntarily stretch or yawn.

The Yang Qi fa exercise is not the sort of exercise commonly seen as spontaneous Qi Gong, but it emphasizes an important principle of this style, which is that movement (Yang) comes out of stillness (Yin).

EXERCISE 31: YANG QI FA

1   Sit on a chair, relax, concentrate on dan tian for quite some time. Become increasingly calm.

2   Notice qi moving in your body. Follow the movements of qi with your awareness. Don't intervene; stay passively following.

3   Do this for as long as you want to.

4   End by bringing qi back to dan tian.

Adding outer movements to the inner allows qi to enact its re-balancing processes. So the parade of movements we witnessed in the class – gentle, frenzied, vigorous, rhythmic – all serve in their own ways to re-adjust the energies in the body.

Qi moves to re-balance. Qi moves when the energy system is in balance. Qi is always moving. It is the quality of movement that is different. The more balanced the system, the more regular and subtle the movements. This does not mean that we should try to force regular and subtle movement. Balanced states come and go and Qi helps the return to balance, without forcing.

EXERCISE 32: THE PENDULUM

1   First do some exercises to activate your qi, then stand in the Qi Gong position. Be in touch with your dan tian. Feel your roots in the Earth.

2   After some time, imagine a pendulum hanging from your perineum and swinging to all sides. Keep your legs relaxed. You might eventually experience a slight vibration in your legs. Allow it, but don't force it.

3   Allow the vibration to spread to other parts of your body. If there's an impulse to move or to make a sound, let it happen. At all times, whatever the movement, stay in touch with your dan tian.

4   Try not to identify with or fix onto any specific movement. Let the movements come and disappear as they will. Accept that you are being moved rather than organizing movement.

5   Finish by collecting qi in the dan tian. Stay standing still for some time.

It is not easy to let spontaneous movement happen. We experience embarrassment and shame. It is also difficult to know what is really spontaneous, and we can fall into the trap of organizing graceful and effective – but unspontaneous – movements for ourselves. When we're in a class, we can be constricted by wondering about what we should do and what might occur. We could react by copying someone or by doing a movement that we think we'd like to do or that feels like we're getting it right ... These tactics might help our anxiety, but they counteract the involuntary flow of qi. So again – be patient. Qi will move you sooner or later. When in doubt, stand still and come into the Qi Gong state, and know that sometimes the smallest, least significant movement is the most honest. It's good practice, too, to stay centred and not be distracted by those who are releasing with operatic fervour!

Maybe a helpful distinction here is between reaction and spontaneity. Let's imagine an experience to see how this distinction works. We're back in a spontaneous Qi Gong class. This one is run by Zhixing Wang so we will follow the instructions as if we were there.

EXERCISE 33: CREATING THE ICON

1   Bring one hand in front of the centre-line of your chest, the thumb-edge towards the body and the little-finger edge away from it. The other hand rests, palm downwards, next to the hip. Settle yourself in this position, breathing. This stylized position, this 'icon' is a blue-print or a reference point, to which you can return as a focus of stability and discipline.

2   Turn inwards, embracing all that you find without judgement. Allow sounds and movements from within to start expressing themselves externally. Whenever you feel yourself acting according to thought, will or expectation, go gently back to the icon position, be still, relax and breathe and wait, empty and patient, for the next spontaneous movement.

3   Close by collecting qi in dan tian.

This exercise illustrates the paradoxical discipline of spontaneity, and how to discriminate it from the rather more predicable and safe route of reaction. If we resist reaction by not copying, and by not inventing a movement to keep up with everyone or because it feels right, there might just be a moment where we notice that our body has moved without pre-thought. Perhaps the head turned, and this caused an effect elsewhere – the shoulder responds maybe. The temptation then might be to grab onto the movements – at last! – and repeat them or self-consciously elaborate them. The art, the discipline, is to let this temptation move away, and instead become willing and available for movements and sounds of the inner landscape to make their way through to the external. Obviously there will be a tricky period while spontaneity and reaction jostle each other, but slowly over time, we tune into a deeper level and become used to following the inner dance as it unfolds in unexpected, unpredictable, not always conventionally attractive ways. There's always the icon, the reference to return to, the standing meditation, maintaining a fixed position so that unknown inner energies can use this position as a point for activation and communication.

This state, we could say, is being in the Tao, or existence in the present. Most of us come in and out of this, and the poignancy and humanity of the practice is that we witness, and directly experience, our own variable attempts to return to our own clear nature – a calm pond, a clear sky, a moment of being where all is well.

On the deepest level, spontaneous Qi Gong is a way of being really true to our unconditioned nature, where we are free of comparison, expectation or desire, and also momentarily free of the interference of what other people are doing or expecting us to do, and free from the interference of our own conditioned voices, which tell us what should happen and in what way. This state, we could say, is being in the Tao, or existence in the present. Most of us come in and out of this, and the poignancy and humanity of the practice is that we witness, and directly experience, our own variable attempts to return to our own clear nature – a calm pond, a clear sky, a moment of being where all is well.

Spontaneous Qi Gong affects us on many levels: the energy-system is re-adjusted, blockages are cleared, charged emotions are released and we are introduced to the self-healing capacity of Qi Gong in an experiential way.

There are arguments that spontaneous Qi Gong is dangerous and can send people to mental hospitals, or to casualty through injury. Indeed, there are some words of caution needed.

✦ Make sure you are in a class with a reliable and trusted teacher.

✦ Even if vigorous movements happen, stay connected with your dan tian.

This means that you express your anger, but don't act out. You are rooting in your centre, watching energetic and emotional phenomena as they happen. The dangers are not really due to the activity itself but to losing the wise eye (your own) upon proceedings, or forgetting to inform your teacher if there is a vulnerable area where you might lose your centre.

If you have suffered from a traumatic accident or emotional experience, or have been severely shocked, it might be wiser not to provoke the organism to remember the event. The provocation might result in you being confronted with a huge flood of emotions that are not easy to handle without a therapist's help. If you should happen to connect with a deeply buried and shocking event, take it for safe handling to a trusted practitioner.

A Qi Gong master once said that he did not consider spontaneous Qi Gong as 'proper' Qi Gong, as there is too much acting out without reference to the middle position. We do not agree. The middle position is not a static place. It is perfectly possible to go into extreme states as long as there is an inner observer, an outer observer, an identification with the dan tian and solid rooting into Mother Earth.

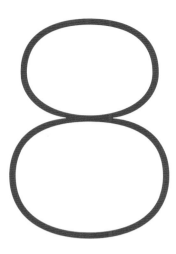

Healing with Qi

As far back as our ancestors go, human hands, eye contact and presence have carried the most powerful potential for healing. A mother holding a child, a hand on an aching belly, a friendly arm around the shoulder, a quiet presence listening without judgement to sorrow or difficulties. This contact has always happened, and still happens, in the most ordinary and spontaneous of ways.

There have also always been members of tribes and communities distinguished by their capacities for healing. These healers, as well as using herbal and mineral medicine, rely mainly on energy healing. The healing rituals may be different – South African bushmen combining ecstatic dance with energy healing, South American shamans sucking out malevolent energy from the patient's body, a healer from the Philippines working with energy surgery – but the basic pattern is the same. Healers use their energy – or, to be more correct, they transmit universal energy – to re-balance the energy field of the patient. In China, as in many cultures, sickness was seen as an imbalance of energy – inside the body or concerning the relationship to the outside world. In this model, the body is not seen as a mechanical entity with different working parts, but a profound system of communication, interaction, relationship and exchange, both within and beyond physical borders.

Until now our emphasis has been directed towards Qi Gong as a method of preventing sickness and maintaining health. Qi Gong was, and is, also used for curing illness. Since the 1950s, there have been Qi Gong clinics in China and a growing interest in 'medical Qi Gong'. There is a substantial body of research into the effects of Qi Gong, in line with the Government's desire to strip Qi Gong of its esoteric and philosophical components and reduce it to a sober medical tool. Some of theses studies were kept secret or not published. An added difficulty is that reports range from the anecdotal to the scientifically rigorous. Currently work is being done to translate and review these studies. Much work is still to be done to verify the results under more explicit scientific standards.

Many books on Qi Gong include claims, substantiated or vague, of success in healing serious illnesses like cancer or Aids. Spectacular healing might occur, but these incidents should not be taken as the norm. On the other hand, there is a spectrum of ailments generally known to be responsive to Qi Gong: hypertension; headaches and migraine; digestive disorders such as constipation; asthma, bronchitis and tuberculosis; arthritis and osteoporosis; emotional distress, depression, fatigue and insomnia. A major feature of Qi Gong is its capacity to boost the immune system. Even if Qi Gong is sometimes used in a symptom-orientated way, it is essentially a prevention-rather-than-cure method. By keeping the qi freely flowing, by balancing the body's energies, the immune system is strengthened. While the main emphasis is on avoiding illness, the effect of Qi Gong on the immune system can also be seen as supporting healing and convalescence.

Healing with Qi Gong happens in three ways.

✦ Self-healing through practice.

✦ Guided self-healing. A Qi Gong healer or teacher selects certain exercises according to diagnosis, and the state of the patient, and brings them together in a specific sequence for the patient. In comparison with a normal Qi Gong practice programme, the patient would practise more intensely, sometimes for many hours. Mostly practice consists of the same exercises as in 'normal' Qi Gong. Special exercises have been developed for certain diagnoses. The famed Madame Guo created a Qi Gong healing programme based on her personal experience of self-induced recovery from cancer through intensive practice.

✦ Healing with external qi. Healers send qi directly to the patient. As we have said, this qi is not 'theirs': they become willing conduits for universal qi and, within this framework, use certain procedures to balance the qi-field of the patient, to take stagnant and poisonous qi out of the system and to re-establish free-flowing energy.

These last two methods are usually combined, and this is most effective. With certain patients – those who have no experience of Qi Gong, those who are too sick or too weak to do their own practice, or those who are in acute crisis – only external qi is applied, while the patient remains passive and receiving.

The 'channels' through which external qi is transmitted are different according to the diagnosis of the patient and the capacities of the healer. The healer sends qi:

✦ Through lao gong: the point in the centre of the palm. Bend your fourth finger back into the palm. Where the fingertip touches is the location of this point.

✦ Through 'sword-fingers'. Point your second and middle fingers forward. Fold the fourth and little fingers back, and hold them against your palm by the thumb pressing down on the fingernails.

✦ Through one finger only.

✦ Through the eyes.

✦ Through the 'third eye'.

✦ Through the mind.

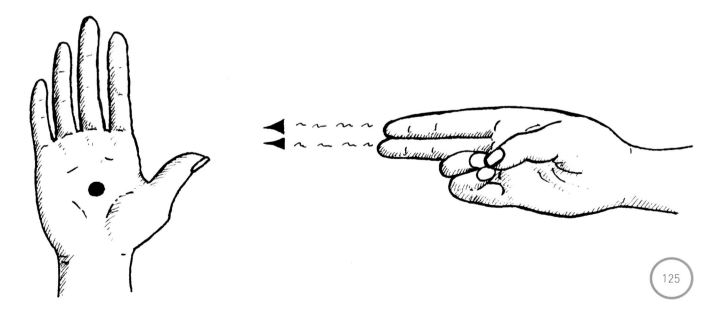

The lao gong method is used rather over an area; the sword-fingers allow qi to move more pointedly, more specifically and deeper into the body. The last three procedures can obviously only be done by very experienced and gifted healers.

If the hands are used, they are usually held about six inches away from the body. The distance is adaptable in each case, depending on the nature of the sickness, the sensitivity of the patient and the qi-strength of the practitioner. Qi is usually sent to the sick parts of the body, to acupuncture points, and sometimes to the whole body. If the treatment is to do with removing stale or poisonous qi, as in traumatized or painful areas, plucking movements are used, as if the bad qi is pulled out of the body, and shaken off from the fingertips afterwards.

For the patient, the experience can be the same as when practising Qi Gong or receiving acupuncture. There are feelings of heaviness, stretching, numbness, warm or cold sensations, discomfort or relaxation and relief. Sometimes there are especially cathartic effects like emotional outbursts, wild dancing, shouting and shaking – responses we know well from shamanic healing and modern body psychotherapy. Imagine a hose-pipe lying loosely on the floor, when suddenly the tap is switched on and water flows in. The hose-pipe leaps about unpredictably as the force of the water enters. The same happens when stagnation is undone and needy areas are flooded with qi. Stories about miraculous healing appeared first in the West, along with Kung fu movies, when the Silk Curtain was still more-or-less closed. The emphasis was not so much on Qi Gong as an easy-to-learn method, but on healers with extraordinary capacities. An early first-hand report of various phenomenal qi-based happenings can be found in Eisenberg's *Encounters with Qi.*

The spirit of investigation, of open-ended enquiry and humility is the background in which you could experiment with energy-transmission exercises. Try them out carefully, trust your experiences and those of your partner.

However, we want to move from the separation of Those who Have It, to the commonality of all. Each of us emits qi – whether we want to or not, whether we are aware of it or not. The question for each is: what kind of qi am I sending to the world? We think that everybody is able to send healing qi under certain conditions – even without knowing any details about meridians, the character of qi and so on. But not everyone is a natural born Qi Gong healer; not everyone has the will and capacity to train to the point of healing excellence.

So what do we need to bear in mind when we engage ourselves as healers, even on the simplest level of offering energy to a friend? The spirit of investigation, of open-ended enquiry and humility is the background in which you could experiment with energy-transmission exercises. Try them out carefully, trust your experiences and those of your partner. At the same time as aligning with this essential curiosity, we want to acknowledge that healing is a complex event. It is obvious that you don't do your energy transmission exercises with severely sick people or even try to 'heal' them in order to replace an adequate therapy. Allow the sending of energy to happen through you, let go of your individual need for achievement or success. Protect yourself, friends and colleagues from an agenda-laden intention to heal. It is sometimes easier to heal others than to heal ourselves; so be aware of when you need healing yourself and are instead trying to 'heal' others.

Finally, we want to comment on the potentially exhausting nature of healing others, if we are not self-protective and aware. Imagine jump-starting another's battery if yours doesn't have much juice in it to begin with! Think also of times when you have made yourself available to someone, soaked up their woes and seen them walk refreshed out of the door, leaving you exhausted and debilitated. If you bear these essential practicalities in mind, you are better prepared for the nonetheless rewarding process of being part of healing. We need to be practical even when we trust the Source. Look after yourself by receiving qi from another when you need it, by practising body-breathing while you are sending energy, by strengthening your energy-field through the Standing Exercise or other exercises that allow you to re-fill your 'batteries'. If you want to engage more seriously in healing you have to learn to safeguard yourself consistently against unwanted energies while you are working, and to acquire methods for cleaning out your 'system' after working.

Let's come to the exercises now. The first exercise originates in body psychotherapy where it is used to activate the energy that flows up and down the body (longitudinal energy flow). This is a useful exercise for reinforcing the experience of taking in Heaven's Qi from above and Earth Qi from below. It is done in a group of three.

EXERCISE 34: LONGITUDINAL ENERGY FLOW

1   One person lies down on his/her back and is asked to relax and imagine sinking down with the out-breath. Partner one sits behind their head and, after a short time of waiting, cradles it. The second partner sits at the feet of the lying person, holding them and preferably contacting the yong quan points (see page 100) at the same time that partner one touches the head.

2   The person who is being treated is asked to stay relaxed and simply experience the energy flow. The 'working' partners should choose a comfortable seat in order that they stay relaxed, too. They concentrate on sending energy through their hands.

3   The 'working' partners keep their hands quiet in this way for at least 10 minutes. After this they take away their hands, while the treated person stays lying down for at least another 2–3 minutes. The lying person keeps the eyes closed throughout the whole exercise, if this feels okay.

4   Rotate, doing this exercise for all three people.

This exercise can be done in combination with the Meridian Circle. The lying person follows the circle internally while being held by the others.

Our second exercise can be done in two variations – either with one partner or in a group of any size.

EXERCISE 35: BUDDHA'S HANDS BRING BACK SPRING

Let your partner lie down on a massage table or on the floor. Stand next to him/her and prepare yourself well by rooting yourself in Heaven and Earth. Imagine not using your personal energy for sending qi but being open for universal qi to flow through you.

1   First engage in cleaning. With the in-breath move your hands, facing downwards, up to the shoulders of your partner. For this upward movement your hands sweep alongside the body, not over it. When you breathe out, your hands sweep directly over the body (about six inches distant) all the way from shoulders to feet. While doing so you concentrate on cleansing your partner's body of used, dirty or sick qi. Afterwards you might want to shake the bad qi out of your hands and make it disappear deep into the earth. Repeat these cleaning movements for some minutes.

2   Begin to send good and healing qi. This time start with your hands right over the body (six inches distant) while breathing in, then go down over the body while breathing out, all the time concentrating on sending qi with your lao gong. Do not go higher than the shoulders because the head is a very sensitive zone, and your partner might get dizzy if too much qi is transmitted. Repeat the sending of qi for several minutes.

3   End the session by holding both hands over the dan tian of your partner for some time.

The group version of this exercise is simplified. It does not include the cleaning part: so be sure that the group members do the cleaning individually before starting, for example by doing the shaking exercise.

EXERCISE 36: GROUP ENERGY SHOWER

36

The group members stand in a circle near to each other. One after the other goes to the middle of the circle and stands there with closed eyes. The rest of the group members direct their palms towards the person in the middle. Slowly they move their hands up and down the body of the person in the middle from shoulder to feet. They all send qi so that the person in the middle receives a qi shower. The distance of the hands to the body of the middle person doesn't matter so much here – it depends on the size of the group.

Even when people have not had any contact with Qi Gong, they are deeply moved by the intensity of the energy field created by the group. This is a good way to end a Qi Gong class, supplying each group member with an extra charge of energy to take home.

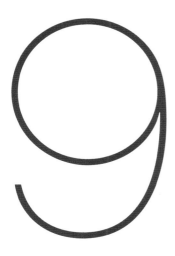

Integrating Qi Gong into Daily Life

PRACTICE WITHOUT PRACTICE

The more regularly you practise Qi Gong, even in small doses, the more you benefit from it. At the same time, Qi Gong does not have to be restricted to formal practice, it can become part of your life in a more organic way. Isn't it true that Qi Gong is already part of your life without being called Qi Gong? You spontaneously stretch, yawn, rub an aching head, or a tired face, massage a stiff neck, rub you hands or your eyes, breathe deeply ...

After some continuity of practice, Qi Gong takes you deeper into energy experiences. As you further embody the principles of Qi Gong, the impact subtly starts to work its way into your everyday life. You sense how your life energy waxes and wanes, how you retain balance and lose it, and how you root into Mother Earth and Father Heaven. Your energy-system will start to function in a different way.

Without going back into formal practice you can reinforce the effect of this unconscious energy-process. Consciously screen your energy state from time to time! This brings you back to your centre, and helps you cope with difficult situations, such as feeling stuck, bored, depressed, angry, under stress, having to deal with demanding people. Simply holding this awareness of your energy-state – turning your eye inwards and scanning your body – is generally helpful enough. Sometimes you might want to reduce negative effects further by allowing breathing to become natural, loosening tension, being aware of your dan tian and your stance, and reassuring your Earth roots by breathing through the yong quan (see page 100) points.

Qi Gong can be done anywhere, anytime. 'Heal' your headache by visualizing a black cloud and then breathing it out, whether you are in the office or walking home; rub your shoulders and between the shoulder blades if you've been in front of the computer too long; rub your face and around your eyes for refreshment when you are tired. Choose from the variety of self-massage, breathing and relaxation exercises to re-connect you with grounded life energy. There might even be space for doing the Qi Gong stance or the shaking exercise in your tea-break! And you can use the time after work on the bus, subway or train to practise the Microcosmic Orbit. After a demanding working day this will give you a way of calming down and re-generating your qi before coming home.

The effect of living with Qi Gong in the everyday has a pleasurably disconcerting way of creeping up on you, from the inside. It's like a relationship where you each live in a different house, and then – how did it happen? – realize that you have moved in together. This synthesis presents itself paradoxically: in one way you are more in touch with your life as you live it, more willing to take responsibility for it – not so much should, as want to. You are also more surrendered to the endless play of Tao. You are responsible for your life, but you surrender your will to the will of the Tao. And you live this union of contradictions, gradually absorbing ways of managing disturbances, also being more willing to accept that they are present as part of how things are. Whatever is happening – whether you are shaken with grief or fear, or soaring upwards with joy – you can breathe into the dan tian and stabilize yourself, consolidating the anchor that holds you throughout all energetic happenings.

DOING QI GONG IN NATURE

It is wise to replenish your energy system as often as possible in nature. Some of us probably have a favourite place which is so full of intense qi that it is just natural Qi Gong to be there, to breathe and to walk. Flowers and trees have potent qi fields. Master Li, from whom we took the following exercises, thinks of these as good teachers. Their power comes out of stillness – as our qi is activated when we are in stillness.

EXERCISE 37: MAKING A QI CIRCLE WITH FLOWERS (LUNG VERSION)

37

1   Stand in front of flowers that attract you. Relax. Your hands should be near the flowers when you lift your arms slightly.

2   Spread your thumb and second finger. Point them towards the flowers. Imagine qi flowing from the flowers into the thumb and second finger of your left hand, up the left arm, through the lungs and out through the right arm and right thumb and second finger.

3   After some rounds, change direction.

You and the flowers form a circle in which your used qi is drawn out, and fresh and renewed qi taken in.

EXERCISE 38: MAKING A QI CIRCLE WITH FLOWERS (HEART VERSION)

1 Extend the middle and the little fingers. Bend the other two fingers back to the palm in a loose fist, and place the thumb firmly over them.

2 Breathe in the same way as before, through the extended fingers, this time guiding the qi through the heart instead of through the lungs.

Trees are universal symbols for being rooted, demonstrating the cycles of life, growth and death. In nearly all cultures, trees are part of rituals and ceremonies. Tai ji and Qi Gong are abundant with tree-language: rooting, moving your arms like branches in the wind, standing like a tree. Different trees have specific healing, nourishing and cleansing effects for specific organs: pine for liver, gall-bladder and eyes; willow for stomach and spleen; poplar for lungs; beech, linden and plane for heart; cypress for kidneys.

EXERCISE 39: MAKING A QI CIRCLE WITH A TREE

Stand near to a tree that attracts you. Relax. Be aware of its qi field, its power, breath and movements and how it pulls you.

1   After some time, lift your arms as if embracing the tree. Take its qi in through your crown, let it flow down inside your body to the soles of your feet.

2   Send used qi deep into the earth, where, in a composted and re-cycled way, it enters the roots of the tree.

3   Once more, take in fresh qi generated by the tree.

4   Go through this circular process as long as you want to.

After doing these circles you may actually lean on the tree and embrace it. Or you might want to lean your back against it. Experiment with what feels good for you.

THE BEDROOM ARTS

Sexuality and Qi Gong? We are looking at two faces. One is beautiful: poetic and instructive texts about love-making, or descriptions of the path of alchemy in erotic language, the sacred marriage of Yin and Yang. The other face is the ugly one – more hidden – of patriarchal control and domination, where the natural order of a free and mutual interplay between Yin and Yang is manipulated into a pattern where women submissively offer up their sexual energy so that men might feast on it and remain forever youthful, strong and in control.

To the Chinese, love-making is the human enactment of the Great Law of Yin and Yang, the interplay of masculine and feminine energies. Erotic language and illustration were used to teach the principles of Inner Alchemy, the inner fusion of masculine and feminine.

Early Taoists seemed to have had a rather uncomplicated and inclusive attitude towards sexuality. They thought that a good sex-life, 'The Arts of the Bedroom', was important for health and that the suppression of sexuality harmed both body and mind. As ever pragmatic in approach, the Taoists avoided debate about the morality of sexuality, devoting their attention instead to the exploration of its nature, and of ways to use and refine it. Cultivating and refining sexual energy would act as inner medicine to strengthen, heal and rejuvenate body and mind, leading to everlasting youth and immortality. The more subtle approach tells of transformed sexual energy leading to spiritual rather than physical immortality: identification and union ultimately with the immortal.

In Eastern religions sexual icons and archetypes which demonstrate the workings of Cosmic Law abound: Shiva and Shakti in their embrace of each other, or erotic paintings on Tibetan thangkas. To the Chinese, love-making is the human enactment of the Great Law of Yin and Yang, the interplay of masculine and feminine energies. Erotic language and illustration were used to teach the principles of Inner Alchemy, the inner fusion of masculine and feminine. By bringing together Yin and Yang, water and fire, ultimately a state is reached beyond dualism, a mystical experience of the unconditional, or the One before Two.

Some masters of Qi Gong not only work with inner sexual imagery but advocate sexual practice as a potent form of Qi Gong. 'Dual Cultivation', Tantra or sexual yoga have been Qi Gong practices since ancient times. Other masters insist that the Sexual Way is the wrong way, hazardous, and that unless followed with discipline and knowledge, it can be harmful, physically and emotionally.

For male Qi Gong practitioners, whether they practise sexual yoga or not, there's a dilemma about ejaculation. (For women there is no such dilemma. Physical orgasm is considered healthy for the whole body-mind.) According to Chinese medicine, ejaculation means losing qi, because jing, the raw essence of qi, is found in sperm. The Chinese answer to this dilemma is ejaculation control. In ages past, the Yellow Emperor was told by his trio of advisors, the Plain girl, the Select girl and the Dark girl, to refrain from ejaculation, to transform sexual energy by drawing it up the spine, thus refining the highly activated, rough jing into subtle qi and shen. A first consequence of this control is that the man experiences sexual energy as an intense stream which spreads throughout the whole body-mind instead of being fixated only to genitals and orgasm. As a second consequence, he is more able to satisfy his partner through prolonged or more frequent sexual activity, balancing thus the slower rhythms of Yin with the faster rhythms of Yang. The beautiful face manifests itself in the description of how the male Yang fire is cooled down, and the female Yin water is heated up. There are exquisitely poetic and minutely detailed texts on love-making and following these texts could be a profound education for men and women, leading them to question their habitual sexual responses.

By bringing together Yin and Yang, water and fire, ultimately a state is reached beyond dualism, a mystical experience of the unconditional, or the One before Two.

In opposition to this potential for sensitive love-making, the ugly face comes in, bringing with it the hidden fear behind the techniques of ejaculation control, fear of the power of Yin, the power of female sexuality and its mythical, inexhaustible nature. In this framework, ejaculation is seen as the loss of power, followed by weakness, and domination of the man by the woman. This hidden fear is then counter-acted by a replacement of the mutual giving and receiving in a loving relationship by a vampire-like attitude, a greedy need to absorb another's energy for one's own empowerment. We have legendary stories of women sucking men dry of their energy (fear), and of men soaking up female essence from countless young women (power). There are still discussions, in all seriousness, about how many female partners a man needs in order to maintain an adequate state of nourishment by female qi. This is not about love, but about power. The abuse of Yin through the excesses of Yang, where patriarchy tries to undermine and control Yin through the domination of women, is a disrespect of the Tao, a refusal of the Yang to live the dark eye of Yin within itself. At the same time, attitudes of revenge, castration and humiliation from women to men polarize the duality even further. Fear of the dark and powerful waters of Yin brings about a wish to control and dominate; fear of the burning and light-bringing fires of Yang brings about a response of defensiveness and aggression. These are opposites in fear of each other, not the necessary creative tensions between Yin and Yang which manifest themselves in many ways through decades and generations, and through all the variations of sexual practice.

For us in contemporary times, perhaps the ejaculation/loss of qi theory is too mechanical. It doesn't take into consideration the kind of sexual relationship you are in, and that, if it is a loving one, you receive from a sexual embrace more than you could ever lose from ejaculation. So there are no ready-made recipes. Explore the issues, and decide for yourself!

It's most likely that your sexual energy will improve through Qi Gong practice. You can decide to enjoy this just as it is, or consider engaging in sexual yoga or Dual Cultivation, bringing a specifically Qi Gong focus into your sexual experiences.

If Qi Gong is practised simply as a fitness or health technique, there's probably no issue around sexuality. Equally, a teacher might ask you to avoid sexuality – usually for 100 days – when you begin to learn Qi Gong, to let you investigate the effects of this abstinence upon your energy. Other teachers may suggest abstinence for a certain time when you begin a new phase, such as the Microcosmic Orbit. This helps you experience your qi in a more specific and focused way.

It's most likely that your sexual energy will improve through Qi Gong practice. You can decide to enjoy this just as it is, or consider engaging in sexual yoga or Dual Cultivation, bringing a specifically Qi Gong focus into your sexual experiences. If you are considering the art of Dual Cultivation, take as a necessary starting point that you are in a loving and healthy relationship, and reasonably aware of those parts of you which would want to act out power needs and other unrelated personal agendas within sexuality. The awareness coming from Qi

Gong practice could illuminate the process of some of these elemental and psychological forces within us, but it also might not. Sexuality is a complex synthesis of the physical and energetic with the cultural, emotional and spiritual, and if your sexuality is wounded, exploration with a professional might be best. It is one thing to improve your sexuality, and another to do Tantra, even if new age Tantrists tell you it's the same. Each is distinct and acceptable in its own right. Tantra is a spiritual path, not an aid to improved sexual function. If sexuality is inhibited by guilt and anxiety, or its patterns of expression harmful or distorted, these restrictions require careful and delicate bringing to consciousness and can't be immediately 'transformed'.

Sexuality is a complex synthesis of the physical and energetic with the cultural, emotional and spiritual, and if your sexuality is wounded, exploration with a professional might be best. It is one thing to improve your sexuality, and another to do Tantra.

Let's come to the traditional Deer Exercise, dedicated to the animal with the most abundant sexual energy, according to the Chinese. There's a version for men, and one for women, and the exercise can be practised whether you are heterosexual, homosexual or celibate. Sex is seen as a natural way of moving and cultivating jing. The Deer Exercise creates these effects without sexual activity – it was recommended for the monks of old and is recommended for those who currently choose celibacy. In this context the libido-effect is a by-product; the exercise can equally be practised to cultivate libido.

EXERCISE 40: THE DEER (FEMALE VERSION)

1   Sit on the ground or on a cushion, cross-legged so that one heel is against the opening of the vagina and putting gentle pressure on the clitoris. The other foot rests on the shin.

2   Rub your hands firmly together and then place them against your breasts. Lightly stroke the breasts in a circular way, initially up towards your face, then outwards and down. You are not rubbing or moving the breasts, but massaging them.

3   Afterwards, put your hands on your thighs, in loose fists – thumb contained within. Contract your perineum, but don't stop breathing. (If this is difficult, contract your anal and genital muscles and keep on breathing.) Hold the contraction as long as is comfortable, and then relax.

4   Repeat the contraction and relaxation as often as you want to.

Do not practise this exercise when menstruating or pregnant. Also, according to the Chinese, this exercise is supposed to aid fertility. Bear that in mind if you're not interested in falling pregnant!

There's an issue about menstruation: as men are told to refrain from ejaculation so as not to lose qi, women are sometimes told to stop or shorten menstruation. (Menstruation, pregnancy and menopause are times when women lose qi.) If the Deer Exercise is used to control menstruation, it needs to be done frequently and for a long time. We do not recommend manipulating the menstrual cycle, seeing it rather as a healthy, natural rhythm.

EXERCISE 41 : THE DEER (MALE VERSION)

1   Sit naked on the floor, on a cushion or on a chair.

2   For this exercise your penis should be erect. With one hand, cover the testicles, the thumb lying on the inner, lower end of the penis; with the other hand massage your belly in soft, circular, movements. After some time change hands and the direction of the movement.

3 & 4   As in the female version.

Finally – avoid fixation on instruction! Let your sexuality inform your Qi Gong and your Qi Gong inform your sexuality. Evoke the Three Treasures, blend Fire and Water, so that belly, heart and spirit combine in one seamless continuum.

EXERCISE 42: FIRE AND WATER

Sit on a chair, cushion or on the floor. Relax.

1   Be aware of your heart: smile at it and let it smile back. After some time breathe out with the Heart
    sound: Hhhaaaaaa ... Continue until your heart feels warm and open.

2   With the next in-breath focus on your third eye, breathing in golden light through the third eye to your
    heart. While you go on breathing out with the same sound guide the warmth and the love of your heart
    down to your genitals. If you want to, place one hand on your heart, the other on your genitals.

3   After some time breathe in through your genitals bringing up sexual energy to your heart. While still
    exhaling with the sound, allow both energies to synthesize in your heart.

4   End by bringing Fire and Water together in your dan tian.

FINDING A TEACHER

Clearly the first choice is to learn Qi Gong with a teacher. If you can't find one, you could start through videos,
tapes and books.

There are no general rules in terms of finding a teacher: there are good female and good male teachers, there
are good Chinese, American and European teachers. How to choose? It depends on the kind of Qi Gong you
want to learn. Most teachers cover a variety of active and passive Qi Gong, usually with a strong emphasis on
one or the other. If you want to engage in meditative Qi Gong, for instance, it is unlikely that you will feel
comfortable with a martial arts Qi Gong teacher.

You can learn Qi Gong individually or in a group. Individually you get more attention
from the teacher whereas in a group the loss of this is balanced by your being in a
stronger qi field – that of the group members and the teacher.

Some schools like The Healing Tao (Mantak Chia) or the Wild Goose (Michael Tse) have an explicit curriculum telling you how to progress in your learning. Most other teachers don't – but then, Qi Gong learning is circular rather than linear. You come back to the same, but always in a new way. Qi Gong mind, beginner's mind. Nonetheless, it's easier to start in a beginners' group rather than plunging into the middle of an advanced class.

You can learn Qi Gong individually or in a group. Individually you get more attention from the teacher whereas in a group the loss of this is balanced by your being in a stronger qi field – that of the group members and the teacher.

Checking if a teacher is good for you is a highly individual affair. You can ask about qualifications, but this is only a formal requirement. With the rest you have to trust your heart, intuition and mind. If you feel well in the presence of a teacher, if your qi flow is much better in their presence – go ahead. If you feel blocked and awkward, this might be your resistance or your fear, but equally he or she might not be the right teacher for you.

Be aware of whether or how your questions are answered. A teacher is an expert, and should ideally display not only a mental understanding, but also an energetic understanding of you as a person. On the other hand, take a wide step away from know-alls.

Be wary of heavy promises about your progress – avoid the Enlightenment-in-one-weekend workshops. Be cautious if other teachers or schools are rubbished, which is – sorry to say – not uncommon in the Qi Gong and martial arts field. Be ultra-cautious if you are told that you can learn good Qi Gong only with Master X or that you'll face a terrible time if you leave Master Y. This – we can assure you – is not true.

Ask if you can 'taste' a class, so that you can soak up the atmosphere and observe the movements and the interaction between teacher and students. There are many Qi Gong classes on offer these days, so you might have to spend a little time searching until you have found the one that suits you.

BodyTao – Body Psychotherapy Meets Qi Gong

On stage: QI GONG MASTER, calm, meditative, dressed in soft and comfortable clothes; PSYCHOTHERAPIST, watchful, furrowed brow, chin thoughtfully cupped in hand, Freud, Jung and Reich easily within reach; PATIENT, looking mistrustful, anxious and aggressive.

The Qi Gong master begins. 'Very angry energy; looks like there is something wrong with the liver. Cleansing exercises ... healing sounds ... Above all, the patient must relax.'

'All very well,' says the therapist, leaning forward, 'but if you don't attend to the source of the anger – in this case his relationship with his father – you're only dealing with symptoms. What about the cause? You have to look deeper.'

The Qi Gong master smiles. 'Ah yes, everyone has a story. We could go round endlessly in stories. So what? This is human nature. Far better to deal with the what than the why. Deal with the energy, not with abstract ideas about the origin of his disorder.'

'What you don't see', responds the therapist 'is that there is energy in the story. Until it unfolds, until you trace the events that have created pain and distress, energy is stuck in self-defensive patterns, addiction or self hate.'

'Inner smile', says the Qi Gong master. 'This is the best approach to self-hatred. Smile at the liver, smile at the other organs ...'

'Too simple!' cries the therapist, 'anyone can pretend to be smiling. And the pain goes underground ... not understood, not clarified by investigation.'

The discussion goes on and on, the silent patient begins to yawn ... and then falls asleep.

149

BODY PSYCHOTHERAPY AND QI GONG WORKING TOGETHER

Qi Gong and psychotherapy ... strange bedfellows? An alchemical marriage? Either/or, or both/and? Do I work on my lung qi to get rid of my depression or do I work it through in therapy? We think that combining both approaches is best. Meanwhile, modern psychotherapy – especially body psychotherapy – not only explores the psychological story or analyzes the transference from patient to therapist, but sees the correspondence between, sees the unity of, emotions, body and energy.

The common ground between Qi Gong and bodypsychotherapy is energy. Qi. Life, and our particular passage through it, shapes our energy-system in a unique way. Body psychotherapy explores this shape in the present – how it prevents us living our energy more fully – and tracks its patterns to the past.

Of course, not everyone needs psychotherapy or Qi Gong. On the other hand, psychotherapy is not only for those in desperate mental or emotional states, as Qi Gong is not only for those suffering from chronic illness. The common ground between Qi Gong and body psychotherapy is energy. Qi. Life, and our particular passage through it, shapes our energy-system in a unique way. Bodypsychotherapy explores this shape in the present – how it prevents us living our energy more fully – and tracks its patterns to the past. How did this shape come into being, and what story does it tell? Qi Gong meets this shape in the present – offering a Way to regain unobstructed qi-flow and return to a more natural and healthy way of being.

If you stand with raised and tense shoulders, holding your breath, your head drawn down and your eyes wide, you will probably experience anxiety. A body psychotherapist as well as a Qi Gong therapist would examine this and other postures and work with energy-blocks, to encourage gradual release of tension. Both would work with the breath, looking for inhibition, and giving support for the breath to flow in a more natural way. After some time the obvious symptoms might disappear.

A different level of work opens up if the therapist has also encouraged the patient to tell her story – the story that unfolds with the melting of energy-blocks. A woman with intolerable anxiety attacks in the middle of the night was given simple Qi Gong breathing exercises and the Microcosmic Orbit parallel to weekly therapy sessions. Beyond the healing effect of these exercises we knew they would also give her a tool for coping with the anxiety, to counter-act the belief that she was the helpless victim of a mysterious sickness. While fighting symptoms, we know also that symptoms are a potent voice for the self and need to be listened to, not simply eliminated. This anxious woman's symptoms told her story: she'd had a very active, extrovert life, engaging strongly in her career, avoiding deep relationships. She'd had an absent father and a weak mother, for whom she had to take responsibility at a very early age. The message needing to be heard and carried by the anxiety attacks was: *You can't have your whole life under control. Even if you stream-line it, by always being perfect, there are wounds, weaknesses, difficulties and disappointments to be acknowledged – and if you don't do so, WE – the anxiety attacks - will remind you.* When this message finally came through to awareness, work could be done on a more general and powerful level, supporting the client to surrender to Yin – to the dark waters of her inner feelings – and then to re-balance her Yin and Yang.

psychotherapy enhances Qi Gong through the ability to listen to an individual story. It also offers a sensitive, personal way of dealing with energy blocks and resistances.

In this way, psychotherapy enhances Qi Gong through the ability to listen to an individual story. It also offers a sensitive, personal way of dealing with energy blocks and resistances. It is important to mention here that East and West have different perspectives and cultural attitudes to the question of individuality, emotions and psychotherapy. We remember a Chinese friend and tai ji teacher recently arrived in Europe, co-leading a therapy group with us. As soon as he had detected a group member with a painfully stiff posture he rushed to her, telling her where to relax and starting to massage her shoulders. We stopped him just as the woman – struck with terror – was about to rush from the room. Our friend had clearly seen the blockages in her posture, but his timing was inappropriate. Major energy blocks or armouring have a meaning, often an existential meaning, which needs to speak, before, during or after the stuck energy is discharged.

If we were not welcomed into this world we either become a rock in order not to feel, or a burning fire so as not to feel the ice. If we were not appreciated for what we are, we start to perform, to avoid feeling like nothing. If we had to stand too early, we have to manage falling anxieties ... If we look at early times, along with the joys of childhood, most of us have been victims, one way and another, to different degrees of pain and severity. Being wounded as a child means being wounded in a most vulnerable state where we cannot protect ourselves adequately. In order to survive we had to block the energy of strange and frightening feelings ... If your father is beating you up and does it even more so when you are crying, you are wise as a child to hold your impulse to hit him back; you are wise not to cry. This was the time of being a victim. But now you are grown up, you have your adult-self to defend you and you can cry if you need to.

Major energy blockages need to be accepted in their useful and protective functions: at the early time, it was necessary to protect yourself by becoming a rock, a fire, a good boy or a good girl.

Therapist and client together have to find a way to accept both realities – the reality of the wounded child; the reality of the adult. Major energy blockages need to be accepted in their useful and protective functions: at the early time, it was necessary to protect yourself by becoming a rock, a fire, a good boy or a good girl. Eventually the client will sense how these defensive patterns restrict energy and life in the present. An inner need arises to go beyond, or underneath. This is the wu-wei point as the client enters into a natural surrender and the therapist gives support by touch, massage and encouragement of feelings.

Psychotherapists are trained to hold and pace this melting process, by containing a client in a stable relationship in which a slow re-parenting, a slow re-balancing of energies can happen. In this place, the blueprint of the Sage is evoked. In the Taoist tradition, the hermits take flight from complicated and sophisticated life, and embrace simplicity in mountains, riversides and forests. We don't have to become cave-dwelling hermits to find simplicity and naturalness. As our energy begins to wake up and move, an inevitable longing arises for the sweetness and relief of coming home; we begin to know that planted in us is the seed of integrity, wisdom, kindness, order and trust – the Five Taoist Virtues.

From a core of acceptance and compassion, we embrace the paradox of changing by accepting ourselves just as we are. We are in the Tao exactly as we have been formed and made. We are in the Tao just as we have been conditioned and worked over by our personal history, genetic inheritance, our parents, tribe, country, belief system, ongoing experiences with others and our work in the world.

We accept that we were wounded, and that we have created defence-systems. The childlike part of us wants to stay small and wants the therapist to be the healing shaman or alchemist – spells and pills please. The Sage in us is interested in the deeper and longer-term effects of the Way of Inner Alchemy. In BodyTao we honour both Sage and child. The Sage is an energy-framework, a conscious and quiet background that holds, no matter what is going on in the world of the child with its change, paradox, turbulence, desire and disappointment. The blueprint of the Sage is embodied deep within our cells.

Let us come to a simple example through which you could taste the interplay of body-psychotherapy and Qi Gong. We invite you into a group that is working with the symbol of the tree.

EXERCISE 43: EXPLORING THE TREE

1   Stand for 5 minutes or longer, without taking a particular posture. Imagine being a tree.

2   Draw a picture showing yourself as the tree you have imagined. Look at your picture alone or with friends. Explore the kind of tree you are … your roots … the ground you are planted in … the space for growth … are there neighbouring trees around you or are you alone … your trunk … branches … do you open up to the light from above?

3   Stand once more imagining Heaven above, Earth under your feet. Feel their energies, let images come.

4   Start to move in a way that your body wants. Does it want to grow higher up, opening up to Heaven? Or does it stamp on the floor, seeking reassurance from the ground? Don't rush: wait until the movement is started from inside. Move as long as you want. Come back to standing still.

5   Imagine your actual father above and your mother underneath. What kind of ground did your mother give you? How did you reach your father?

6   Talk to your father: let the word(s) grow in your chest before speaking out loud. Talk to your mother.

7   Later write down some good and some bad memories.

8   Stand again; imagine your father in front of you; try to visualize his posture, his face. Is there a change in your posture, energy-flow and emotions? When you have finished, do the same with your mother. What is blocked? What about your breath? Which movements want to emerge and are either held or frozen?

9   Do another picture, showing your energy map – indicate flowing and blocked areas in whatever way you want to.

10 End up by standing in the Qi Gong stance, creating universal and ideal parents, feeling their energy and your reaction to it. After some time bring the energy down to your dan tian.

WALKING THE FIGURE EIGHT

Qi Gong can come into the therapeutic process right from the start – it enhances sensitivity towards body posture and energy processes; it activates and cultivates qi and so helps locate obstacles to energy-flow. It comes into its own when de-armouring has started and energy is set free. This freed energy does not flow automatically and suddenly in a harmonious way, even if some therapists seem to think so. Have a good primal scream – and that's it! Energy can erupt in disorderly and erratic forms, and needs to be worked with and refined.

An emotionally disturbed person usually has a disrupted Yin/Yang pattern – either/or rather than both/and. On an advanced therapeutic level Qi Gong is excellent as training to re-enter a flowing Yin/Yang pattern. To practise Qi Gong or tai ji is to learn about alternating Yin and Yang, breathing in and breathing out, falling and rising, contraction and expansion. In BodyTao we use the principles of Yin and Yang in a simplified way, calling it 'Figure Eight'.

A client in his late 30s: designed from childhood to be mama's crown prince who would save her from the rough and unsophisticated ways of his father, he developed a rather gentle, understanding and polite personality to live up to this expectation. He was not able to live his maleness, his aggression, competitiveness, roughness. Because he was not at home in his male strength, his soft and yielding behaviour was inauthentic. We found him hovering uncertainly in the middle field of his Yin/Yang spectrum.

He started the session complaining about a rude friend of his who was unashamedly aggressive to people. This is where the therapist's thoughts wander ... What does he really want to tell? His envy of the other's determination? The fear of being rude and egotistical himself? The need to prove to therapist/mama/papa that he is a good boy and the other one is bad? There had to be a way to bring all these energies which he projected out there back to him.

Dividing the room in half, we asked him to play the rough one in one half and himself in the other. He enjoyed enacting his softness, understanding and sophistication in contrast to the rude and stupid macho man.

After we asked him to concentrate more on body movements in the role-playing there was a shift. As the bully, he began to enjoy his strength and power, finally threatening to ' steamroller the softy like a worm'. Pleasure in the release of this rude energy! At the same time he hesitated – understandably – before playing the about-to-be-steamrollered worm.

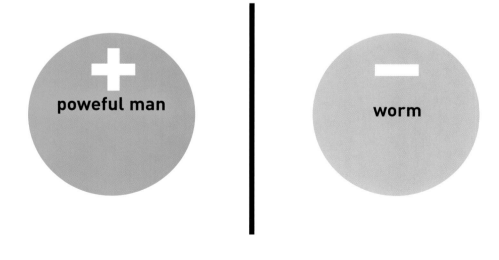

Again there was a shift – a surprising shift! - when he finally enacted the worm. Diving into beautiful and organic caterpillar movements he reconsidered the power of the rough one as 'stiff' and 'rude'.

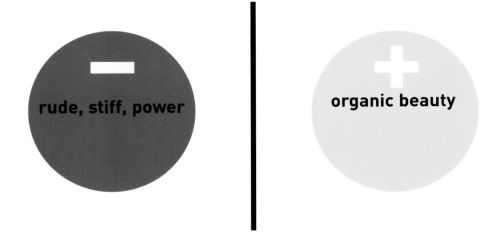

Asked at this point to step back, and to define the two roles in a non-judgemental way he described his experiences with the rough one as 'bringing the power to the point' and the experiences with the soft one as 'taking a bath in your energy'. He could now hold both energies without discarding one. The next step – integration.

We showed him how to walk a Figure 8 in the room, to be aware of the feelings in each part of the circles – the near slopes and the far slopes – and at the middle point, marked by a cushion.

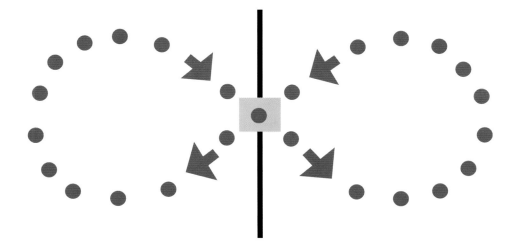

The client liked the alternating rhythms of the two states very much, the gradual growing of strength and determination and then coming back to the middle point; the gradual diving into letting go and softness, and coming back to the middle point. As he could always come back to the centre, he wouldn't get lost in aggression or in surrender.

To reinforce the experience we worked with him in a movement sequence integrating both fields. It ended up as a wriggling-shaking worm movement through the whole body, flowing into a punch with the right fist into the open left hand, at the same time stamping with the right foot.

You might discover in yourself a particular polarity, where you only live one half, having sent the other one to the Kingdom of Shadows. As soon as you accept the whole spectrum, in comes the beginning of freedom, flow and effortlessness. As you let go of attachment to only one half and stop fighting, you can stop being defensive. You don't have to be strong all the time and fight weakness in yourself and others; you don't have to be helpless and weak, always stopping strength in yourself and others. You are in your centre and remain in your centre even when you walk the two sides of the 8. This process is called transformation: from two to one.

CULTIVATING EMOTIONS

Taoists agree with most body-psychotherapists that there is an energetic core of positive feelings in us. Borrowing from Reich, let's see ourselves as a circle with three layers.

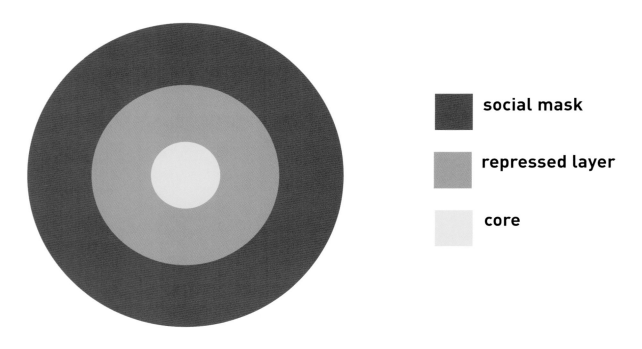

social mask

repressed layer

core

Remember our client: his social mask is sophistication, softness and understanding; in the repressed layer we find envy, feelings of inferiority and egotism; in the core we see him as a loving and beloved being.

From the Taoist perspective once again ... the Five Virtues. Not acquired by effort – as the word Virtues might suggest – but part of the immortal soul and manifest in the natural state of being. Virtues are closely related to organs, they live in them. If the organ-energy is healthy, the Virtue is strong, and vice versa. If the organ-qi or Virtue is disrupted, this is the time of the negative emotions; the organs then function as doorways – as unwilling hosts – for negative emotions.

Qi Gong in itself supports emotional health by deepening breathing, cultivating energy flow and re-shaping posture. Relaxation is a powerful therapeutic procedure – even if we don't share the Chinese optimism that it will heal all emotional disturbances eventually! But now: how to deal with 'negative' emotions and with repetitive, dysfunctional patterns? The Chinese way is to get rid of negative emotions by relaxing, by breathing them out, by positive visualization and by strengthening and cultivating the Virtues. This might help with momentary emotional turbulence but we think emotional trauma and disorders that are rooted in early childhood and 'built into' the personality need more.

Go back to our three-layer circle. What do we find in this toxic middle layer? If our early behaviour didn't fit into family norms and expectations, these characteristics had to be thrown in the dustbin. If angry protest was forbidden – into the dustbin. If love was not answered – into the dustbin. If sadness was discouraged – into the dustbin. If joy was ridiculed – into the dustbin. These repressed feelings and energies – like all organic waste – have their own life. Organic waste + oxygen = life-giving compost. Organic waste cut off from oxygen, becomes mouldy, foul, smelly and toxic. In psychotherapy we bring the 'oxygen' of awareness and compassion to this middle layer. And incidentally, the blame we inevitably heap upon ourselves for having this toxic material, is adding waste to waste. It is inevitable that we harbour discarded energies. The point is to become aware of them (oxygen), face them and take responsibility – without blame.

To be aware and responsible means:

✦ not acting out, not releasing our feelings in an impulsive and compulsive way;

✦ not suppressing them.

Back to Qi Gong. The Healing Sounds exercise opposite is standard in dealing with emotions. Our ecological adaptation suggests compost – not waste! Instead of 'throwing out' bad energy (where is it going to go?) we rather transform it, through awareness and acceptance, into the Virtues. As feelings are closely connected with organs, this is also an exercise to clean and balance the inner organs. We start with a list combining elements, organs, colours, feelings and Virtues, based on the theory of Five Elements or Five Major Forces.

ELEMENT	metal	water	wood	fire	earth
ORGAN	lung	kidney	liver	heart	spleen
COLOUR	white	black or dark blue	green	red	yellow
EMOTIONS	sorrow sadness depression	fear	anger aggression	joy restlessness	pensiveness self pity
VIRTUES	integrity courage	gentleness inner wisdom	kindness	love order	trust

EXERCISE 44: HEALING SOUNDS

Sit down, relax. Keep your arms gently resting on your thighs, palms up. Breathe naturally.

1   Visualize your lungs, feel them moving with the in-breath and out-breath. Smile at them. Be aware of sadness, sorrow and depression without judgement. After some time, exhale slowly with the sound sssssssss on the out-breath with your tongue touching your teeth. Gently let go of sadness, sorrow and depressed feelings. Stay sitting still, let white light surround your lungs, while you transform the sadness into courage and integrity.

2   Go to your kidneys, smile at them. Be aware of your fears. Try to accept, don't judge. Eventually, with the next slow exhalation, round your mouth as if blowing out a candle and made the breathy sound wooooooooooo. Gently let your fears go. Allow a silky blue colour to surround the kidneys, transforming fear with gentleness and inner wisdom.

3   Visit your liver, smile at it. Be aware of anger and aggression. Accept it, don't judge. Eventually with a slow exhalation make the sound sssshhhhh. Feel whether you are ready to let go of anger and aggression. Allow a green light to surround your liver, transforming anger into kindness.

4   Visit your heart, smile at it. Be aware of excitement and restlessness. Don't judge. Eventually, with a slow exhalation, make the sound hhhaaaaaaaa. By accepting restlessness you might transform it into love, peace and inner order. The colour red is surrounding your heart.

5   Visit your spleen, smile at it. Be aware of pensiveness and self-pity. Try to accept, don't judge. Eventually, with a slow exhalation, make a guttural sound whooooooo, like an owl hooting. As you let go of pensiveness and self-pity, a yellow colour surrounds your spleen, transforming self-pity into compassion and love.

Repeat any of these sounds as often as you want to. If the 'transformation' does not happen, stay cool. Emotional processes need time. Don't fret about results: it is more important to become aware of the energies involved in your emotions.

May the qi be with you!

11

Interviews with Master Zhixing Wang
and Master Li Zhi Chang

Q

How would you advise a beginner to find a good Qi Gong teacher?

Zhixing Wang: You just have to try and find out. Everyone has a basic sense and sometimes you just feel it – it happens and in the right time. That's the way I found my teacher.

Li Zhi Chang: The teacher need not be famous or the author of many books. Look rather for clarity and evidence of ongoing practice.

Q

How often and how long should you practise? Does the practice have to be correct? Can you do too much? Can Qi Gong be dangerous or harmful?

ZW: It depends on your purpose, what you want to achieve with Qi Gong. If you want to study Qi Gong seriously, twice every day is the minimum standard requirement. Nowadays people want Qi Gong more as a way to help their life, to increase energy, to keep well and get rid of problems. For these purposes you don't have to be too rigid. Regular practice, two or three times a week, or from time to time having a good session. I feel that sometimes if there's too strict a requirement this gives people a negative impression and some people get frustrated and give up. So you need to integrate practice into your condition and circumstances. If you can do it more regularly you can benefit, but even one good session a week can keep it going – like the TV that's on standby, but can be switched on.

In terms of correctness, there are two ways of looking at this. If you're practising on a technical level it has to be right. These requirements are pretty strict. This way of practising takes a longer time. After a while the penny drops, the fruit falls and you have the benefit. Like driving a car, learning to swim, you build it into body-consciousness. I call this post-natal Qi Gong. The other level which we can call pre-natal or Shen Qi Gong is a matter of inspiration, a matter of initiation. There's less technical requirement, qi is within everybody. You already know how to do it. The teacher gives you the initiation. This doesn't take much to learn – you realize the nature is within you, but you need guidance. This is like Information Technology rather than Mechanical Technology.

LZC: The times of daily exercise depend on your purpose and level of experience with Qi Gong. If you are advanced you might need only half an hour's practice a day, at the same time, out of your own interest, using all possibilities for remaining in the Qi Gong state. If you don't believe in Qi Gong you could practise 10 hours a day without effect. If Qi Gong is used for healing you might have to practise longer. You can't practise too much as Qi Gong is a way back to the natural. You can't harm yourself as long as you are following the instructions and practising correctly.

In the beginning it is difficult to do the exercises correctly because you are learning. For a master practitioner, it is essential to be correct, but, even as a beginner, with ongoing practice, your qi will start to correct you. There are a hundred ways, all flowing into one.

Q

Is there any sort of person you wouldn't teach? Is there any kind of person who shouldn't practise at all?

ZW: Generally, Qi Gong should be open to everybody, particularly if it's a matter of life and saving people, you would accept anybody. On a practical level, people often choose themselves, by not coming, by switching off. In China some teachers would not want the responsibility of severely ill cancer patients or mentally disordered people, although in principle these people would benefit.

LZC: This depends on the motivation and inner attitude towards Qi Gong. If people don't believe in Qi Gong, if they don't practise, if they have a wilful resistance against it, there is no point teaching them.

Q

Do you work with emotional states too?

ZW: A feature of Qi Gong is that it is powerful and effective to change people's emotional states and to heal emotionally rooted problems. In a Qi Gong class in China it is quite standard to hear people crying or laughing. In my Hua Gong method there's a particular part focused on emotional blocks, to understand emotions and to work on a very deep emotional transformation.

LZC: There are specific methods for people with emotional problems. For example, with depression, you need to work with the upper chest, freeing the energy blockages there. At the same time there needs to be guidance on the soul level, to bring an element of lightness into the emotional situation.

In the case of people with psychosis, great care should be taken. The teacher needs to be experienced and the patient needs to be more constantly monitored and guided by the teacher.

Q

Is there a difference working with Chinese or Western people?

ZW: I see the differences more on an individual than a cultural level. In nature we are all the same. But on an artistic and practical level if you see it as a special kind of skill or ability there probably is a difference. Once I opened up a magazine and there were Chinese who were demonstrating and some Western Qi Gong teachers too. The grace and softness and a mellow quality was more evident in the Chinese. On that level, it takes generations to come into consciousness.

LZC: Obviously there are cultural differences and different ways of thinking. But these are less important than an essential sensitivity and motivation for learning which is beyond culture.

Q

Does Qi Gong have a different effect for men and women? Why are there so few female Qi Gong masters?

ZW: The general effects should be the same. But of course men and women are just so different – we needn't prove that! In a way there has to be a difference There are more male teachers because men are more active in presenting themselves and making things happen in society – it's not because women teachers are less good. I met a woman teacher who had a great impact – and there is the Wild Goose style teacher, and the famous Madame Guo.

LZC: Women might have more basic sensitivity to Qi Gong; men rather have the capacity for focused concentration. The fact that there are fewer female teachers is due to cultural attitudes about the roles of men and women.

Q

What would you advocate in terms of sexual behaviour for Qi Gong practitioners?

ZW: If you practise just to keep well, the requirement on the sexual level doesn't have to be too strict. If you want to become an expert, an artist or master, this is a different story. The traditional point of view says you should stop sexual activity for 100 days. I had this training myself and it really made a difference. If you are practising martial or medically orientated Qi Gong this is important. Or for some people who are weak or ill it is draining to be too active in that way. If it's a natural and spontaneous approach, you tune in and feel – you develop your sensibility.

LZC: For both men and women it is good to have sexual feelings, but these should not be brought too often to a high point. After sex it is important to recover properly and to re-collect qi, for example taking 3-5 minutes for body breathing. Avoid subsequent strenuous activity. Naturally a harmonious relationship is helpful in maintaining a good qi-field.

Q

How and when did you come to learn Qi Gong?

ZW: I was in the University, studying intensively and my eyesight was deteriorating quite badly. This was in the early 1980s, the time after the Cultural Revolution when the tradition had begun to revive. I copied some exercises from a magazine and my eyesight improved so that I didn't have to wear glasses anymore. I followed the technique but didn't really feel the energy. Then I did a simple way of practising with basic posture and some imagination and this had quite a good effect. Even though it was difficult to concentrate – I was writing my dissertation – when I came out of meditation I felt in a different state of consciousness. A few years later I met a Qi Gong teacher and my wife and I had treatment with him. This was my first experience of feeling the qi. That was 1984 and we were amazed by the power, had never felt it before. Then my wife and I trained with Master Zhang Hong Bao. We were very impressed by his power and effect and the energy he could manifest, just through talking. He gave simple approaches and powerful transmissions. I always respect him as my Master. After that I kept to the practices but it felt as if the qi was practising me. Like a 24 hour practice. I would wake from sleep and in the middle of the night find myself in a lotus position. I would meditate for a long time and in the morning find myself lying down on the floor, freezing cold. All sorts of strange and powerful experiences. When I started teaching I taught what I had learned but I was already practising different things because of the way the energy led me. So I thought why don't I teach what I am practising? Then the name Hua Gong came through like a very strong mind wave.

LZC: I learned as a little boy, primarily from grandather and father. As in the Chinese custom, I accompanied them to all activities. So I learned to practise Qi Gong – the term 'Qi Gong' was not used at the time, it was simply called 'practice'. Up to 18 I was very active in all kinds of sports like table-tennis, boxing, fencing. After 18 there was full concentration on Qi Gong.

Q

Are you always in the Qi Gong state? What is it like to be so full of qi?

ZW: Yes – you feel that qi is practising you – it's a state of being you are always in. Sometimes we fail to be aware of it – but how can we not be connected to cosmic energy? Actually it's funny to say connect as the connection is always there. Rather we should say to activate the connection. Like the TV when you're not watching it is switched off but still connected. You can still be exhausted but this doesn't affect you as it might usually, you are not defeated or overwhelmed. There can still be a rhythm – sometimes you are vibrant and at other times more contained, more settled. The thing is not to reject one way and prefer the other – but it feels as if there's a layer between you and the problem. You're more detached, you're observing at the same time.

LZC: At an early age – about 15 or 16 – I felt full of qi. Afterwards I realized that I have ongoing choice about being in the Qi Gong state or not. Now I feel that Qi Gong is practising me.

Q

How would you explain the teacher's qi field? How do you use it?

ZW: The teacher provides a medium for people to activate the connection and the teacher's qi field helps people become inspired and plug in for themselves; I work basically from my heart, from my qi and body experience.

LZC: Some teachers create the qi-field through thought, others through sending qi. I do it once only, by 'thinking', by circumscribing the group, creating a 'plate' or circular qi-field for all the members of the group.

169

Describe your special Qi Gong style. What makes your style different from other styles?

ZW: Hua Gong is a way to point to our true state of being. When we are unaware of that state, it's as if we are a TV or computer not plugged in. This is a waste of potential. We could all be so much more if we plug into a greater system, a greater information network, a pool of cosmic energy and information. In my understanding some teachers in China are teaching on a similar level but probably expressing it differently.

LZC: Quiet Qi Gong is not about just sitting down and being quiet, it is to do with cutting off the six Yin roots (eyes, ears, nose, mouth, body and thought) so that in this stillness, Yang, the spirit, can arise. So it is not enough simply to sit still, you have to cultivate this quietness. To still the body alone, is to complete only the cutting off of one root. Stilling the six roots can bring about an inner state that is characterized by the arising of spirit and spontaneous thinking.

What features are common to all Qi Gong styles? What is your opinion of Quiet Qi Gong (to Zhixing Wang), and of Spontaneous Qi Gong (to Zhi Chang Li)?

ZW: The common features are that basically Qi Gong works on a subtle or insubstantial level. This subtle approach affects the physical body more powerfully than any physical approach. You could work very hard in a physically vigorous way and this wouldn't necessarily affect the insubstantial and the spiritual. To work on the mental, consciousness level is more in the very nature, the very core of the Qi Gong method. Everything else is on a complimentary, secondary basis.

LZC: If anyone wants to have success in Qi Gong, they have to cultivate stillness. In some methods this principle is lost, because there is only movement. Movement is a part of Qi Gong but it has to be soft, slow and natural. However, spontaneous Qi Gong can be a good method and form of practice. It is like steering a boat through rough sea, until it becomes calm again.

12

Information

alchemy: Outer Alchemy (Wai Dan) refers to the transformation of outer materials (minerals, herbs) to produce the outer elixir; pills and drugs to reach longevity or immortality: Inner Alchemy (Nei Dan) refers to the inner elixir; to contact the immortal soul by cultivating the Three Treasures jing, qi and shen through Qi Gong and meditation.

crown: baihui, Heaven's Door, the top of the head; crosspoint of du mai with a line from ear to ear.

dan tian: elixir field; 'dan tian' (without location) means lower dan tian in the area between the navel and pubic bone; it is an energetic centre and the centre of gravity, where qi is collected and refined; mostly three dan tians are described: upper dan tian, situated at the root of the nose between the eye-brows ('third eye'); middle dan tian, situated in the middle between the nipples on the breast bone; lower dan tian.

du mai: Governor Channel, main Yang channel: begins at perineum, flows up over the spine and over the head, ending at the upper palate.

jing: essence, germ, subtle substance; sexual energy; the Yin aspect of qi; full of potential.

lao gong: acupuncture point in the middle of the palm; used for sending and taking in qi; bend your fourth finger into the palm, the fingertip touches lao gong.

martial arts: wu shu, umbrella concept for the innumerable outer styles (eg Shaolin Kung fu) and inner styles (eg tai ji quan, bagua quan).

meridian system: complex system of energy pathways, networking the whole body.

Microcosmic Orbit: basic exercise in quiet Qi Gong, connecting du mai and ren mai into a circle.

ming men: Gate of Life, located on du mai opposite the navel, between the second and third vertebrae.

qi: life energy, life force.

ren mai: Conception Channel; main Yin channel; begins at the perineum, runs up over the front middle-line, ending at the tip of the tongue.

Shaolin: Buddhist monastery, built in the 5th century; the legendary birthplace of hard Qi Gong and Kung fu.

shen: most subtle Yang aspect of qi; spirit, mind; refers to ordinary as well as to spiritual consciousness.

shou gong: ending exercise.

tai ji quan: ancient movement sequence, enacting tai ji, the harmony and unity of Yin and Yang. Originating as a martial art, it is also done for health and meditation; there is a variety of styles – best known are Chen, Yang and Wu; in 1956 the Beijing style – a shorter and simpler version of Yang style was developed.

Three Treasures: jing (essence), qi (energy) and shen (spirit).

triple burner: triple heater; body function without correspondent physical substance, regulating water and energy in the upper, middle and lower parts of the body.

wu-wei: 'non-doing'; not forcing; non-interference with the natural course; spontaneous action, free of attachment and intention.

Yang: originally, the sunny side of the hill; active, creative, masculine, outer, moving aspect; it is a relative concept.

yi: imagination, consciousness, will, intention; the focusing and guiding function of the mind in Qi Gong.

Yin: originally, the shady side of the hill; receptive, passive, female, inner, still aspect; it is a relative concept.

Yin-Yang: primary polarity; the two primordial principles of Nature: the balancing forces of cosmic order in the manifest world.

yong quan: 'bubbling spring'; connecting with Yin, Earth qi; located on the sole of the foot – one third of the way from the base of the second toe to the heel.

LIST OF EXERCISES

1 Exploring Qi

2 Warm-up Sequence

3 The Return of Spring (Shaking Exercise)

4 Relaxation along Four Lines

5 Meditative Self-Inquiry

6 Qi Gong Stance 1

7 Qi Gong Stance 2

8 Qi Gong Stance 3

9 Holding up the Sky

10 Watching your Breath

11 Breathing with a Partner

12 Breathing in Intervals

13 Body Breathing

14 Guiding Qi

15 Lotus Flower

16 Ending 1

17 Ending 2

18 Circling the Ball

19 Punching

20 Carrying the Moon

21 Reaching and Grounding

22 Flying Wild Goose

23 Preparation for Quiet Qi Gong

24 MicroCosmic Orbit

25 The Crane takes Water

26 Smiling 1

27 Smiling 2

28 Breathing in Nine Segments according to the Buddha

29 Belly Circles

30 Simple Meridian Circle

31 Yang Qi fa

32 The Pendulum

33 Creating the Icon

34 Longitudinal Energy Flow

35 Buddha's Hands Bring Back Spring

36 Group Energy Shower

37 Making a Qi Circle with Flowers (Lung Version)

38 Making a Qi Circle with Flowers (Heart Version)

39 Making a Qi Circle with a Tree

40 The Deer (Female Version)

41 The Deer (Male Version)

42 Fire and Water

43 Exploring the Tree

44 Healing Sounds

BIBLIOGRAPHY

Beinfield, Harriet and Korngold, Efrem: Between Heaven and Earth, A Guide to Chinese Medicine,
New York: Ballantine, 1991

Cohen, Kenneth S.: The Way of Qigong, Bantam Books, 1997

Chang Jolan: The Tao of Love and Sex, Wildwood House, London, 1984

Chia, Mantak and Maneewan: Awaken healing light of the Tao,
    Healing Tao Books, Huntingdon, New York, 1993

Cooper, J.C.: Taoism The Way of the Mystic, Aquarian Press, 1984

Eisenberg, David: Encounters with Qi, Penguin Books, 1985

Eliade, Mircea: Myths, Dreams and Mysteries, Collins, 1976

Eliade, Mircea: Shamanism: Archaic Techniques of Ecstacy, Collins

Frantzis B.K.: Opening the Energy Gates of your Body, North Atlantic Books, 1993

Guori, Jiao: Qigong Yangsheng, Medizinisch Literarische Verlagsgesellschaft, Uelzen, 1988

Hammer, Leon: Dragon Rises, Red Bird Flies, Crucible, 1990

Kaptchuk Ted J.: Chinese Medicine. The Web that has no Weaver, Rider, 1985

Kit, Wong Kiew: The Art of Chi Kung, Element, 1993

Lao-Tzu: Tao te Ching, Translated by Stephen Addiss and Stanley Lombardo,
    Hackett Publishing Company, Indianapolis, 1993

Li Zhi-Chang: Mit dem Herzen lächeln, Heyne Verlag, München, 1999

MacRitchie, James: The Chi Kung Way, Thorsons, 1997
    Chi Kung, Cultivating Personal Energy, Element Books, Shaftesbury, 1993

Ni, Hua-Ching: Tao The Subtle Universal Law, The Shrine of the Eternal breath of Tao,
    Malibu California, 1980

Olvedi, Ulli: Yi Qi Gong – Das Stille Qi Gong, Barth Verlag, München 1994

Reid Daniel: Chi-Gung. Harnessing the Power of the Universe, Simon and Schuster, 1998
    The Tao of Health, Sex and Longevity, London: Simon &Schuster, 1989

Tse, Michael: Qigong for Health and Vitality, Piatkus, 1995

Veith Ilza: The Yellow Emperor's Classic of Internal Medicine,
    The Williams and Wilkins Company, 1949

Watts, Alan: Taoism Way Beyond Seeing, Thorsons, 1999
    Tao: the Watercourse Way, Pantheon, New York, 1975

Wilhelm, Richard: The Secret of the Golden Flower, Arkana, Penguin, 1984

CONTACTS

United Kingdom and Europe

Zhixing Wang
Chinese Heritage
15 Dawson Place
London W2 4TH
Tel/Fax: 020 7229 7187
Ask for a list of accredited instructors. The models in this book, Francesca Harvey and Dario Gerchi are on this list.

Michael Tse Qigong Centre
PO Box 59
Altrincham WA15 8FS
Tel: 0161 929 4485
Fax: 0161 929 4489
Tse@qimagazine.com

See Mantak Chia under USA and Canada for directory of international Healing Tao instructors

If you are interested in Taoist philosophy and practice
The British Taoist Association
Peter Smith (Secretary)
16 Birch View
Epping CM16 6JT
Tel: 01279 833 2325

USA and Canada

Qigong Research and Practice Centre
(Director Kenneth S Cohen)
PO Box 1727
Nederland CO 80466
Tel: 303 248 0971
www.qigonghealing.com

Tse Qigong Centre
PO Box 2697
Kirkland WA 98083
Tel: 425 823 0199
Fax: 520 441 6578
Mtse@wildgooseqigong.com

Mantak Chia
The Healing Tao Centre
PO Box 1194
Huntingdon
New York 11743
Tel: 717 325 9380
www.healing_tao.com
Ask for a directory of international Healing Tao instructors

Taoist Studies Institute
225 N. 70th Street
Seattle WA 98103
Tel: 206 784 5632

Liang Shou-Yu
6500 *4 Road
Richmond
BC
Canada V6Y 2S9

Qi: The Journal of Traditional Eastern Health and Fitness
PO Box 18476
Anaheim Hills CA 92817
Tel: 714 779 1796
www.qi-journal.com

Networking Groups
Qigong Institute
561 Berkeley Avenue
Menlo Park CA 94025
Tel: 650 323 1221

Germany

Li Zhi-Chang
Karl Marx Ring 41
D 81735 Munich
Tel: 0049 89 69341002
Fax: 0049 89 69341003

BodyTao workshops: www.bodytao.co.uk

UK
Barbara Brown
BM BodyTao
London WC1N 3XX
bodytao@dial.pipex.com

Germany
Dr Günter Knöferl
Am Fluss
Lindengasse 3
D 90419 Nuremberg
Tel: 0049 911 262255
taotao@lau-net.de

Artist

All the illustrations in the book were done by Jutta Garbert, Qi Gong teacher and illustrator
Tel: 0049 911 6105993
juga@odn.de

INDEX

Page numbers in *italics* indicate exercise
instructions

abstinence/celibacy 142, 143, 168
acquired (post-natal) qi 11
active & passive polarities,
   identification with   78-80
active Qi Gong 59
   exercises
      Carrying the Moon *88-9*
      Circling the Ball *83-4*
      Flying Wild Goose *94*
      Punching *85, 86-7*
      Reaching & Grounding *90-2, 93*
air (breath/Yang) qi 11, 15
alchemy 27-8, 173
animal energies & forms 23-5
anxiety, healing techniques 150-1

baihui (Crown/Heaven's door) 99, 100, 173
balance 2, 117
Belly Circles *108-9*, 110
belly (dan tian) breathing 64, 108
benefits of Qi Gong 2-5, 135-6
bloated feeling 74
Bodhidarma 29
Body Breathing *67*
body-mind interaction 68
body psychotherapy 149-54
BodyTao
   anxiety therapy 150-1
   cultivating & working with emotions 160-3, 166-7
   exercises *154, 163*
   releasing energy blocks 150-1, 152
   role of body psychotherapy 149-54
   Walking the Figure Eight *156-9*
breath (air/Yang) qi 11, 15
breathing
   Buddha 106-8
   dan tian (belly) 64, 108
   difficulties 74
   embryonic 67
   exercises
      Body Breathing *67*
      Breathing in Intervals *66*
      Breathing in Nine Segments According
        to the Buddha 106, *107*, 108
      Breathing with a Partner *65*
      cautions 65
      Watching Your Breath *64*
   natural 2, 62-4
   paradox (hard belly) 66-7
   pathological (disturbed) 62, 66
   as practice ingredient 35, 36
   qi 106
Breathing in Nine Segments According
   to the Buddha 106, *107*, 108

Buddha breathing 106-8
Buddha's Hands Bring Back Spring 130

Carrying the Moon *88-9*
categories (forms) of Qi Gong 32-3, 59, 95, 170
cautions 38, 65, 121
celibacy/abstinence 142, 143, 168
channels *see* meridians
childhood distress & trauma 151-2, 161
Chinese medicine 7, 15, 26-8
   see also healing & healing techniques; meridians
Chinese/Western practice differences 167
chong mai (middle channel) 16, 106, 110
Circling the Ball *83-4*
classes & teachers 146-7, 165, 166, 169
cleaning 108, 130
coccyx (weilü) 98, 100
collecting qi 72
colours 162
commanding line 18, 19, 68
Conception channel (ren mai) 16, 97, 110, 173
Crane Qi Gong 25, 33
Crane Takes Water *101*
Creating the Icon *119*, 120
Crown (baihui/Heaven's door) 99, 100, 173
cultural differences, practice 167

dan tian, definition 173
dan tian (belly) breathing 64, 108
Dao Yin 21
dazhui (Great Hammer) 99, 100, 111
Deer (female & male versions) 143, *144*
dis-identification 47, 170
disturbances 73-5
Dong Gong *see* active Qi Gong
drowsiness 75, 102
du mai (Governor channel) 16, 97, 110, 173
'Dual Cultivation' 141, 142-3

Eight Brocades 59, 86, 95
Eight Extraordinary (Miraculous) Meridians 16, 110
   see also individually by name eg du mai
ejaculation 14, 141
Elements, Five (Five Major Forces) 162
Elixir Field *see* dan tian
embryonic breathing 67
emotions, cultivating & working with 160-3, 166-7
Ending 1 & 2 72
ending (shou gong) 72, 174
energy *see* qi
energy blocks, releasing 150-1, 152
energy healing 123
'energy work' 2-5
essence *see* jing
essence & principles of Qi Gong 5, 28
exercises
   Belly Circles *108-9*, 110

Body Breathing *67*
Breathing in Intervals *66*
Breathing in Nine Segments According to
   the Buddha 106, *107*, 108
Breathing with a Partner *65*
Buddha's Hands Bring Back Spring *130*
Carrying the Moon *88-9*
Circling the Ball *83-4*
Crane Takes Water *101*
Creating the Icon *119*, 120
Deer (female & male versions) 143, *144*
Ending 1 & 2 *72*
Exploring Qi *8*
Exploring the Tree *154*
Fire & Water *146*
Flying Wild Goose *94*
Group Energy Shower *132*
Guiding Qi *68*
Healing Sounds *163*
Holding Up the Sky *60-1*
Longitudinal Energy Flow *128*
Lotus Flower *70*
Making a Circle with Flowers
   (Lung & Heart Versions) *137, 138*
Making a Qi Circle with a Tree *139*
Meditative Self-inquiry *50*
Microcosmic Orbit 16, 71, *98-9*, *100-2*, 136
Pendulum *118*
Preparation for Quiet Qi Gong *98*
Punching *85, 86-7*
Qi Gong Stances 1, 2 & 3 *54, 56, 58*
Reaching & Grounding *90-2, 93*
Relaxation Along Four Lines *48-9*
Return of Spring (shaking exercise) *46*, 75
Simple Meridian Circle 110, *111*, 112-13
Smiling 1 & 2 *103*, 104, *105*
Warm-up Sequence *40-5*
Watching Your Breath *64*
Yang Qi Fa *116*
   see also practice
Exploring Qi *8*
Exploring the Tree *154*

female/male practice differences 167
feng fu (jade cushion) 99, 100, 105
Figure Eight, Walking the *156-9*
Fire & Water *146*
Five Animal Frolics 23-5, 59, 95
Five Elements (Five Major Forces) 162
Five Taoist Virtues 152, 160, 162
flowers, exercises involving *137, 138*
flowers (Taoist term) *see* Three Treasures
Flying Crane Qi Gong 59, 95
Flying Wild Goose *94*
food (Yin) qi 11, 15
forms of Qi Gong 32-3, 59, 95, 170
frequency, time & place of practice 36-8, 165-6

Gate of Life (ming men) 98, 100, 173
Governor channel (du mai) 16, 97, 110, 173
Great Hammer (dazhui) 99, 100, 111
Group Energy Shower 132
guided self-healing 124, 125
guiding mind (Yi) 68-71, 106, 174
guiding qi with Yi 68-9, 71, 106
    exercises
        Breathing in Nine Segments According
            to the Buddha 106, 107, 108
        Guiding Qi 68
        Microcosmic Orbit 16, 71, 98-9, 100-2

hard belly (paradox) breathing 66-7
headaches & dizziness 69, 74, 136
healing & healing techniques
    effects of 126-7
    energy healing 123
    exercises 128, 130, 132
    external qi 124-7
    headaches & dizziness 69, 136
    healers' skills 7, 22, 124-6
    illnesses responding to 124
    'medical' Qi Gong 30, 32, 123-4
    self-healing 124, 125
    spectacular healing claims 124, 126
    stress & tension 69, 75
    see also BodyTao
Healing Sounds 163
heart palpitations 74
Heaven's door (baihui/Crown) 99, 100, 173
Heaven's eye (third eye) 99, 103, 125, 173
    see also upper dan tian
history & origins
    in alchemy 27-8
    Dao Yin 21
    in early Chinese medicine 26-8
    in modern times 30-3
    in monastic tradition 28-9
    name origin 2
    shamanic heritage 22-5, 33
    spontaneous Qi Gong 33, 115
    in yoga 28-9
Holding Up the Sky 60-1
Hua Gong 166, 168, 170
huiyin (perineum) 98, 100

imagery see visualization & imagery
immune system, effects on 124
indolence 75
inherited (pre-natal) qi 10, 67, 98
Inner Alchemy (Nei Dan) 27, 28, 140, 152, 173
inner smile 103-5

jade cushion (feng fu) 99, 100, 105
jewels see Three Treasures
jing 12, 14, 173
    jing/qi/shen relationship 16, 18, 19, 68, 141

moving, with Deer exercise 143, 144
Jing Gong see quiet Qi Gong
jing luo see meridians

lao gong 100, 125, 126, 173
Lesser Heavenly Cycle see Microcosmic Orbit
Li Zhi Chang
    on dis-identification 47, 170
    exercises taught by 97, 100
        Breathing in Nine Segments According to
            the Buddha 106, 107, 108
        Crane Takes Water 101
        Making a Circle with Flowers
            (Lung & Heart Versions) 137, 138
        Making a Qi Circle with a Tree 139
        Preparation for Quiet Qi Gong 98
    interview with 165-70
    Qi Gong learning experience 169
Longitudinal Energy Flow 128
losing qi 14, 141, 144
Lotus Flower 70
lower dan tian (Lower Elixir Field) 14, 98, 100, 173
lying down 52

major ('organ') meridians 36-7, 110, 113
Making a Circle with Flowers
    (Lung & Heart Versions) 137, 138
Making a Qi Circle with a Tree 139
male/female practice differences 167
martial arts, definition 173
'medical' Qi Gong 30, 32, 123-4
meditative Qi Gong see quiet Qi Gong
Meditative Self-inquiry 50
menstruation 14, 144
meridians 15, 36-7, 106, 110-13, 173
    see also Eight Extraordinary Meridians
Microcosmic Orbit 16, 71, 98-9, 100-2, 136
middle channel (chong mai) 106, 110
middle dan tian 99, 100, 173
mind
    body-mind interaction 68
    indolence & drowsiness 75, 102
    psychosomatic field 68
    Qi Gong State 2, 47-50, 169
    restless mind 74, 75
    state of mind during practice 35, 36
    Yi (guiding mind) 68-71, 106, 174
ming men (Gate of Life) 98, 100, 173
monastic tradition 28-9
movement see exercises; posture & movement

natural breathing 2, 62-4
navel (embryonic) breathing 67
Nei Dan (Inner Alchemy) 27, 28, 140, 152, 173
Nei Gong see quiet Qi Gong
'new' Qi Gong 32, 33
non-doing (Wu-wei) 77-80, 152, 174
normal (righteous) qi 10, 15

nose, breathing through the 62-3
nourishing line 18, 19, 68
nutritive qi 15

'organ' (major) meridians 36-7, 110, 113
organs 15, 37, 162
Outer Alchemy (Wai Dan) 27, 28, 173

pain 73
paradox (hard belly) breathing 66-7
paradoxes & polarities, Tao x, 1, 78-81, 152
passive Qi Gong see quiet Qi Gong
pathological (disturbed) breathing 62, 66
Pendulum 118
perineum (huiyin) 98, 100
place, time & frequency of practice 36-8, 165-6
polarities & paradoxes, Tao x, 1, 78-81, 152
post-natal (acquired) qi 11
posture & movement 1, 2, 35, 36, 51-9
    see also exercises
practice
    in & with nature 137-9
    benefits 2-5, 135-6
    breathing techniques used 62-7
    classes & teachers 146-7, 165, 166, 169
    correctness 165-6
    cultural differences 167
    disturbances 73-5
    ending (shou gong) 72, 174
    integration into daily life 135-6
    interactions of major practice ingredients 35-6
    posture & movement during 51-61
    Qi Gong state during 47-50
    role of Yi (guiding mind) 68-71
    sexual considerations 14, 140-6, 168
    Tao of practice 77-81, 136
    time, place & frequency 36-8, 165-6
    warm-up 39-46
    see also exercises
pre-natal (embryonic) breathing 67
pre-natal (inherited) qi 10, 67, 98
pregnancy 144
Preparation for Quiet Qi Gong 98
primal qi 10
principles & essence of Qi Gong 5, 28
psychosomatic field 68
psychotherapy, body 149-54
Punching 85, 86-7

qi xi, 7-9, 15
    in Chinese medicine 7, 15, 26
    cleaning 108, 130
    collecting 72
    cultivating 2
    effects of breathing techniques & exercises
        64, 66, 67, 106, 108
    flow during practice 35, 36, 73
    guiding see guiding qi with Yi

in healing *see* healing & healing techniques
jing/qi/shen relationship 12, 16, 18, 19, 68, 141
losing 14, 141, 144
releasing energy blocks 150-1, 152
in spontaneous Qi Gong 116-18
see also meridians; types of qi individually
by name eg food qi
Qi Gong Stances 1, 2 & 3 *54, 56, 58*

Qi Gong State (ru jing) 2, 47-50, 169
quiet Qi Gong 59, 170
exercises
Belly Circles *108-9*, 110
Breathing in Nine Segments According
to the Buddha 106, *107*, 108
Crane Takes Water *101*
Microcosmic Orbit 16, 71, *98-9*, 100-2, 136
Preparation for Quiet Qi Gong *98*
Simple Meridian Circle 110, *111*, 112-13
Smiling 1 & 2 *103*, 104, *105*
indolence & drowsiness 75, 102
role of Yi 71, 106
sitting posture 52

Reaching & Grounding *90-2, 93*
reaction, compared to spontaneity 118-20
relaxation 48, 161
exercises *48-9, 103*, 104, *105*
ren mai (Conception channel) 16, 97, 110, 173
restless mind 74, 75
Return of Spring (shaking exercise) *46*, 75
righteous (normal) qi 10, 15
ru jing (Qi Gong State) 2, 47-50, 169

Sage, the (Taoist archetype) 4, 152-3
schools (forms) of Qi Gong 32-3, 59, 95, 170
self-healing 124
self-massage 39-45, 100
sending qi *see* healing & healing techniques
sex & sexuality 14, 140-6, 168
exercises *143, 144, 146*
shaking, caused by qi flow 73
shaking exercise (Return of Spring) *46*, 75
shamans & shamanism 22-5, 33
Shaolin Monastery & monks 4, 29, 173
shen 12, 16, 173, 174
jing/qi/shen relationship 16, 18, 19, 68, 141
shou gong (ending) 72, 174
side-effects of practice *see* disturbances
Simple Meridian Circle 110, *111*, 112-13
sitting 52
Small Qi Circle *see* Microcosmic Orbit
smile, inner 103-5
Smiling 1 & 2 *103*, 104, *105*
spirit *see* shen
spontaneous Qi Gong 33, 115-21, 170
exercises *116, 118, 119*, 120
standing 53-9

state of mind *see* mind
'stopping the breath' (embryonic breathing) 67
Storehouse of Treasures *see* Chinese medicine
stress & tension 69, 74, 75
styles (forms) of Qi Gong 32-3 59, 95, 170
'sword-fingers' healing method 125, 126

tai ji quan 59, 95, 174
tai ji slope 108, 109
Tantra 141, 143
Tao, the viii-xi
attitudes towards sexuality 140
communist attitudes to 30, 32, 33
Five Taoist Virtues 152, 160, 162
Golden Age of 26
monastic traditions 28-9
origin of qi 10
paradoxes & polarities x, 1, 78-81, 152
Sage (archetype) 4, 152-3
Tao of practice 77-81, 136
Taoist Trinity (Three Treasures) 12-19, 69, 173, 174
through spontaneous Qi Gong 120
water metaphor 2, 77
Wu-wei (non-doing) 77-80, 152, 174
see also BodyTao
teachers & classes 146-7, 165, 166, 169
tension & stress 69, 74, 75
third eye (Heaven's eye) 99, 103, 125, 173
see also upper dan tian
three belly circles 108-10
Three Treasures 12-19, 69, 173, 174
time, place & frequency of practice 36-8, 165-6
trees
Exploring the Tree *154*
Making a Qi Circle with a Tree *139*
symbolism & imagery 138
triple burner 37, 174

upper dan tian 16, 99, 100, 173
see also third eye

vibration, caused by qi flow 73
Virtues, Five Taoist 152, 160, 162
visualization & imagery 69-71
use in exercises
Belly Circles 108-9
Breathing in Nine Segments According
to the Buddha 107, 108
Exploring the Tree *154*
Healing Sounds *163*
Pendulum *118*
Reaching & Grounding 93
Smiling 1 *103*

Wai Dan (Outer Alchemy) 27, 28, 173
Wai Gong *see* active Qi Gong
Walking the Figure Eight 156-9
warm-up 39-46

Warm-up Sequence *40-5*
Watching Your Breath *64*
water, as Taoist metaphor 2, 77
weilü (coccyx) 98, 100
Western/Chinese practice differences 167
Wild Goose Qi Gong 25, 59, 147, 167
Wu-wei (non-doing) 77-80, 152, 174

Yang *see* Yin, Yang & Yin-Yang
Yang Qi Fa *116*
Yellow Emperor 23, 26, 141
Yi (guiding mind) 68-71, 106, 174
Yin, Yang & Yin-Yang
balancing disrupted patterns 151, 156
day/night relationships 36
definitions 174
dis-identification 47, 170
harmonising 80
Inner Alchemy (Nei Dan) 27
meridians 97, 113
as polarities x, 2, 174
primal qi 10
sex & sexuality 140, 141, 142
spontaneous Qi Gong principles 116
symbol & tai ji slope x, 80, 108
and the Tao xi-x
Three Treasures 19
understanding qi 8
Yin (food) & Yang (air/breath) qi 11, 15
yong quan 100, 111, 174

Zhixing Wang
exercises taught by *90-2, 93, 119*, 120
Hua Gong 166, 168, 170
interview with 165-70
Qi Gong learning experience 168